LOCKS, MA[illegible] MATHEMATICS

LOCKS, MAHABHARATA AND MATHEMATICS

An Exploration of Unexpected Parallels

V. RAGHUNATHAN

HarperCollins *Publishers* India

First published in India in 2013 by
HarperCollins *Publishers* India

Illustrations of locks: Roopalika

ISBN: 978-93-5029-643-1

2 4 6 8 10 9 7 5 3 1

HarperCollins *Publishers*
A-53, Sector 57, Noida, Uttar Pradesh 201301, India
77-85 Fulham Palace Road, London W6 8JB, United Kingdom
Hazelton Lanes, 55 Avenue Road, Suite 2900, Toronto, Ontario M5R 3L2
and 1995 Markham Road, Scarborough, Ontario M1B 5M8, Canada
25 Ryde Road, Pymble, Sydney, NSW 2073, Australia
31 View Road, Glenfield, Auckland 10, New Zealand
10 East 53rd Street, New York NY 10022, USA

Typeset in 11.5/15.5 Electra LT by
R. Ajith Kumar

Printed and bound at
Thomson Press (India) Ltd.

To my friends, without whom life would have been much less fun: Amar, Rajendra, Ravi (Jules) and Sudhir

CONTENTS

PREFACE

What could possibly be the common thread running through locks, the Mahabharata and mathematics? Truth be told, a very thin one! One could conjecture that there would be parallels between locks and certain aspects of coding and decoding techniques in mathematics relating to computer science. But anything beyond must surely feel like a bit of a stretch, especially if one states that one intends to tie stories from the Mahabharata into it as well. And yet, that is what I have tried to do in this book. Why would I try to tie these disparate elements (and therefore put in so much effort into writing it) if the book were merely an exercise in self-indulgence? It is simply to explore unexpected parallels, even if rough, across three entirely different worlds: of an Indian chronicle of epic proportions, centuries-old brilliant craftsmanship manifested in clever devices like locks, and the only absolute truth in the universe – mathematics.

Perhaps the only reason why my idle curiosity got me to loop a common thread through locks, the Mahabharata and mathematics was to indulge in an exercise in divergent thinking. To be able to say, so to speak, that it is possible to find anything if you look for it hard enough! But why these three entirely dissimilar ingredients?

In the case of locks, I have been collecting them for nearly three decades and I know something about old Indian padlocks – their beguiling inner mechanics and beauty; the ingenuity of the locksmiths fashioning them in our forefathers' times, with primitive tools but exquisite skills; and the bastardized metallurgy of ancient India that produced such timeless works of ingenuity. My collection adds up to some 800 different pieces, all in working condition, from the length and breadth of India. And I could not have been amidst them for nearly three decades without some intrinsic fascination with the variety and mystery they represent. The fact is, I discovered an entirely new world when I stumbled upon the intriguing imagination of the bygone locksmiths captured in the timeless contraptions they made.

As far as mathematics is concerned, I am hardly a mathematician, but my deep respect, awe and fascination for it arises from the fact that it is probably the only absolute truth in the universe. As Roger Penrose observes, while observed science may be limited by the constructs of the human intellect, there is no such limitation as far as pure mathematics is concerned. This means, while perceived realities of physics or chemistry, for example, may vary across different universes, $2 + 2$ must always be 4 and $(a + b)^2$ must always yield $a^2 + b^2 + 2ab$ in any universe. Now, isn't that fascinating?

As for the Mahabharata, who cannot but be enthralled by the epic? At one level, it is a soap opera of epic proportions, capable of holding millions upon millions of us glued to our televisions on weekends even in the twenty-first century. At another level, it is a complicated human construct, encapsulating every conceivable nobility and foible humans are capable of, delineating every shade of grey that goes into making the human animal, presenting every conceivable dilemma – or rather, every *difficulty of being good*, as Gurcharan Das would put it.

The common thread across the three worlds was revealed to me for no apparent reason in a burst of inspiration over some four months. I decided to pen down the thoughts as they came, and the result is this book.

However, I must add a word here for the benefit of the readers. The book purports to be nothing more than a simple, fun text, and they will find no other takeaway, apart from an inkling of how completely unrelated things may have some fascinating underlying commonalities. It has no profound insights into how out-of-the-box thinking happens, and adds nothing to the existing body of knowledge about any of the three worlds it explores. The treatment of stories from the Mahabharata is fun and tongue-in-cheek, that of mathematics is equally light – scarcely beyond the high-school level, and the insight into locks just sufficient to hopefully leave readers clicking their tongues, saying, 'Oh I didn't know there was more to padlocks than what we see hanging on most doors.' Also, if the readers expect exact, one-to-one identity, correspondence or congruence between the stories, locks and the mathematical principles invoked in the context, they are bound to be disappointed. And if they wish to enjoy the sense of discovery of the unexpected parallels captured in the book, they will have to stretch their imaginations a bit as well. Expectations of a reader looking for an answer as to why there should be a parallel between only selected stories from the Mahabharata, some locks and some mathematics, I am afraid, are bound to remain unmet! Having said that, I hope readers will share the sense of wonderment I have experienced while exploring the parallels that bind the three non-parallel realms.

Some special individuals need mention. Meena, my best friend and wife, is always the first one I thank, for she always spends hours after hours editing drafts after drafts of my manuscripts. This book has been no exception. My niece Roopalika, an outstanding freelance graphic illustrator and graphic designer who, having enlivened the book by redrawing my photographs of the locks into the beautiful hand-drawn illustrations one sees in the book, deserves my heartfelt thanks. But for her, the book would have been drabber. And no less indebted am I to Krishan Chopra, my editor at HarperCollins, whose exacting standards have doubtless improved the quality of the book substantially. I am equally thankful to Prema Govindan for her outstanding copy-editing support, which has enriched the quality of this book significantly. And finally, my excellent friend Nilofer Suleman (a leading artist) and her daughter Shilo Shiv Suleman (an outstanding designer, illustrator and artist) who have done the wonderful cover of the book. And I am also indebted to my friend Ajit Rangnekar whose gracious comments on my manuscript encouraged me as much as they helped me improve the manuscript.

I would also like to thank Google and Wikipedia, the life-saving search engines to which I turn every time I have to search for my misplaced keys! Given the ease of making quick preliminary reference checks online, I for one – I am not sure about other authors – do often wonder how we were writing books in the BG and BW era. So thank you Google and thank you Wikipedia.

April 2013 **V. Raghunathan**

ONE

DRAUPADI, THE LOCK WITH FIVE KEYS AND POLYNOMIALS

Draupadi's Tall Order

Draupadi is the key female protagonist in the Mahabharata. She ended up with five husbands – the Pandava brothers. There is an interesting story within the epic explaining how this instance of fraternal polyandry came about. One version of the story goes thus.

Draupadi, in her previous life, was a virtuous maiden in a hermitage, but far too ambitious for her own good! As a consequence she could never find a man good enough for her to marry. So she performed rigorous penance to Lord Shiva. And when he appeared astride his bull, complete with a hissing cobra coiled around his neck and a crescent moon upon his top knot, she demanded to be granted a husband with the five highest qualities that anyone could possess, namely, valour, values, muscles, looks and erudition. Lord Shiva, momentarily taken aback, counselled her wisely that such a man was impossible to find; nay, such a being simply didn't or couldn't exist anywhere – heaven and earth included. The good lord advised her that she ought to aim a tad lower. But ambitious ladies in those days were as resolute for the most perfect husbands as they are today. The determined lady would settle for nothing but the best.

Faced with one so obdurate, Shiva granted her the boon, saying – tongue-in-cheek, it would turn out – 'Tathastu! May your matrimonial ambition be fulfilled in your next life!' and did the disappearing act.

Now boons granted by gods in our mythology have to come good, even if the interpretations are stretched like lawyers' truths. The lord had categorically granted that Draupadi would find all the five highest qualities in matrimony in her next life. But we all know the law of nature, which is that men that good simply don't occur in nature – not then, not today – and there wasn't much Lord Shiva or any of the 330 million gods could do about it. So the powers-that-be conspired to make five magnificent men, each endowed with one of the five highest qualities, and thus created the Pandava brothers.

Five-in-one

Yudhisthira was the noblest, the most righteous and just of the five brothers, with a golden complexion to boot; Bhima was a great hulk of a man with extra-long arms and the strength of a thousand elephants, plus he was master of the mace, and never forgot an enemy's face; mighty Arjuna, the master archer, possessed the highest intelligence and valour, and was a stranger to both fear and anger; Nakula, the most good looking of men, with a special way with horses, was an accounting scholar as well; and Sahadeva, a master swordsman, was up there in heroics and chivalry, and was easily the most learned, scholarly and eloquent of men.

By now, you must be getting the angle. But even so, the story of how Lord Shiva's boon came to fruition must be told with a little more flourish.

Duryodhana

We are told that Duryodhana – the chief villain of the epic Mahabharata – and his ninety-nine Kaurava brothers were all cads of varying degrees, and were extremely jealous of their more accomplished, more valiant and more affable cousins, the Pandavas. What is more, Duryodhana took spontaneous aversion to the fact that Yudhisthira was the most probable successor to the kingdom. Nor was his aversion entirely born of avarice, as we shall see presently.

Duryodhana's father, King Dhritarashtra, being visually challenged, was little more than a titular king, and Duryodhana, as the first born of the king, was not unreasonable in being desirous of inheriting his father's throne. Ever since Dhritarashtra's younger half-brother, the childless Pandu – who had once ruled the kingdom on account of Dhritarashtra's blindness – had renounced the kingdom several years ago to perform penance in the Himalayas to redress his childless state, Dhritarashtra had assumed charge of the throne with help from his uncle, the grand sire, Bhishma.

Several years later, Kunti – one of the two wives of Pandu – landed back at the palace in Hastinapura with five sons in tow, of whom she claimed three to be her own and two those of Pandu's second wife, Madri. The eldest of these was Yudhisthira who, along with his four brothers, got busy winning the hearts of all and sundry in the palace circles and outside, on account of their smugly noble qualities – attributes that Duryodhana found abhorrent.

All this caused Duryodhana more worries than he had brothers. Not only were his five loathsome cousins stuck to each other like a bunch of barnacles, worse, the fat fellow Bhima perennially entertained himself swinging his mace about and knocking the bejesus out of the Kaurava brothers whenever it took his fancy. That other fellow Arjuna constantly showing off his archery skills and sucking up to their guru Dronacharya was the limit. Yudhisthira was a tolerable enough bloke, except that he could kill you with sheer nobility and goodness. Thank goodness, the other two, Nakula and Sahadeva, were relatively more modest fellows – with little reason not to be modest anyway.

Duryodhana's worst fear was that Yudhisthira was older to him by the narrowest of margins and was therefore very likely to stake his claim successfully to Dhritarashtra's throne when he came of age. Yes, the threat to the throne had to come from Yudhisthira, especially as the Grand Sire had vowed never to marry and had eschewed the throne in favour of Dhritarashtra.

Under the circumstances, if he, Duryodhana, staked a claim as the legitimate heir, would Yudhisthira and his odious brothers, particularly that burly Bhima, give in easily? Nah.

Understandably, this gave Duryodhana severe insomnia, and the disposition that goes with the affliction. Not that he had allowed his sleeplessness to go entirely wasted. He had been putting those hours to good use, scheming how to deal a crippling blow to his competition. The Pandava princes encountered some mysterious and inexplicable dangers to their lives and limbs every now and then, including a drowning attempt on an unconscious Bhima, poisoned at a picnic of the royal princes. The enquiries having ended the way our CBI enquiries do – though no one attributed the survival to the plump prince's buoyancy – the question of how an unconscious fellow weighed down by heavy stones could resurface hung heavier on Duryodhana than the stones he had used to drown Bhima.

The Intrigue and the Escape

It was a widely known secret, and not necessarily confined within the palace walls, that King Pandu, notwithstanding his wives, Kunti and Madri, could not beget children. So how Kunti bore him three sons, namely Yudhisthira, Bhima and Arjuna, and Madri two, namely, Nakula and Sahadeva, were matters of much speculation during the long and idle afternoons in the corridors of the royal court. It soon came to surface – as such things usually do – that the three sons of Kunti were spawned from the seeds of Dharmaraja (Yama), Vayu, and Indra respectively and Madri's sons by those of the Aswini Kumara twins, physicians to the gods. Well, Kunti, like her sons, didn't endear herself much to Duryodhana, who prided himself on being the legitimate son of his father.

So it seemed reasonable and sufficient grounds to Duryodhana that the lives of the Pandava brothers be comprehensively snuffed out, along with Kunti's. He therefore conspired for them to be sent to the forest resort of Varanavata where great festivities were ostensibly being planned in honour of Lord Shiva. The idea was that once the Pandavas were persuaded by the charms of Varanavata to proceed thither, they would be provided royal comfort in an especially built palace on the occasion, for the duration of their stay during the year-long festivities. The palace, being built entirely of combustible material with liberal quantities of extra-inflammable wax, would catch fire *accidentally* and thus the Pandavas would meet their maker, removing Duryodhana's impediment to the throne. And if all went well, he could even collect insurance on the burnt edifice, who knows; yes he was supposed to be that kind of cad...All in all, not a bad plan, if ends, and not means, are what matter.

However, the Pandavas got some advance information of Duryodhana's plan and escaped in the nick of time, setting fire to the combustible palace themselves, leaving an old woman and her five young sons who had providentially sought shelter for the night at the palace to burn in their stead. There is little record of any heartburn the Pandavas may have experienced over allowing the death of innocents to save their own lives, or of brooding over whether the act wasn't as foul as or maybe worse than Duryodhana's. But we do know that nobody seems to have held the death of six innocents against the Pandavas, though Duryodhana has been much maligned for his plot! In short, the Pandavas' action was considered justified in the interests of dousing any suspicions about their escape from the fire, lest Duryodhana cook up a new recipe for their annihilation. Thus, they escaped using a tunnel they had stealthily dug up earlier for the very purpose, and eventually proceeded to live incognito, in the house of a Brahmin in the town of Ekachakrapura, disguised as Brahmins.

Draupadi's Swayamvara

King Drupada of Panchala, who had always coveted valiant Arjuna for his son-in-law, was most distressed when he first heard of the fire in Varanavata in which the Pandavas and their mother were presumed dead. However, as rumours of their escape drifted into his ears, Drupada arranged for the swayamvara of Draupadi, in the hope that if Arjuna was indeed alive, he would surface, attracted by the prospect of winning the hand of the incomparably beautiful Draupadi. Clearly, Drupada, as the father of Draupadi in this life, had no clue about his daughter's doings in her previous one. His hope wasn't misplaced either, given that the challenge for winning Draupadi's hand in matrimony involved the highest skills in archery, designed to filter out lesser archers – a tactic that, we are told, was also used in the 2G scam. And sure enough, the Pandavas left Ekachakrapura and unerringly headed for Panchala, still in the garb of Brahmins, to take a shot (pun unintended) at the swayamvara.

The swayamvara venue was elaborate. And so was the test designed for the suitors, comprising the mightiest of kings and princes. Duryodhana, Karna, Shishupala, Jarasandha and Salya were all there, as were dozens of other highly eligible royal suitors. Even Krishna had come, probably in the hope of catching up with good friend Arjuna. The test involved stringing a mighty bow while looking down into a pool of water at the reflection of a spinning fish high above one's head, and shooting into the eye of the rotating fish overhead through a narrow aperture, without taking one's eyes off the reflection. That makes cracking the IIT entrance test a pleasant pastime by comparison, doesn't it?

Karna Affronted

Understandably, not even the most valiant of the royalty present came anywhere near stringing the bow, leave alone loading the arrow; never mind shooting into the eye of the furiously spinning fish. Not Duryodhana, though he had fervently hoped to win dusky Draupadi's hand. Not Shishupala. Nobody. Karna – also a son of Kunti, albeit castaway as an infant, being born of a union between an unwed Kunti and the sun god, and subsequently rescued and brought up by a royal charioteer – might have done it. But the beautiful Draupadi forbade him from even trying, pronouncing him unworthy of her royal hand. Moreover, given that even Karna, the progeny of the sun, valiant and handsome as he was, could hardly meet the five qualities demanded by Draupadi in her previous birth single-handedly, it would not serve Lord Shiva's purpose to let him succeed at the swayamvara. No wonder he caused the pretty maiden to pre-empt Karna's participation by publicly humiliating him.

Arjuna Makes His Move

A rumbling of protest started gathering momentum over the virtually impossible assignment. There was also unhappiness at the great Karna being denied his chance. In the midst of the din, a poorly dressed Brahmin strode towards the podium where the apparatus was set up. Poor and weak the Brahmin might have been to a casual glance on account of the privations suffered over a year of incognito existence in Ekachakrapura in a poor Brahmin's home; but it only took moments before his royal and un-Brahminical warrior-like bearing and the shimmering power of his persona made it clear to the audience that this was as much an ordinary Brahmin as Hanuman an ordinary simian. And their anticipation, apprehension and misgivings were assuaged as the 'Brahmin' reached the podium, calmly strung the bow, lifted the bow with the heavy arrow in place, directed it upwards, looked down into the pool of water, drew the bowstring to his ears and let go of the string, as if this was just another day at practice. The assembly was startled by a ringing twang; the eye of the dead fish had been pierced right through the iris.

No one in the assembly was so daft that the real identity of the 'Brahmin' eluded them. Many of those present were happy at this revelation – King Drupada and Princess Draupadi amongst them. And there were those who were equally unhappy – Karna, Duryodhana and his throng among them.

And Draupadi's Wish Is Fulfilled after a Lifetime

Things moved fast from here on. Draupadi promptly garlanded the Brahmin, aka Arjuna, after which the five brothers, accompanied by Draupadi, rushed back to Ekachakrapura to share the good news with their mother. Bhima, the ever-enthusiastic hulk, shouted from the hallway. Something to the effect: 'Ma, look what we have brought!' And Kunti, accustomed to a loud Bhima bringing home the spoils of his hunts, responded perfunctorily, 'Whatever it is, you brothers share it among yourselves as usual!'

And that's how the boon of Lord Shiva and the ambition of Draupadi from her previous life came to be fulfilled. Draupadi, as was prophesied, got the five highest qualities she looked for in matrimony, even if it took a rebirth and five different men to meet her expectations!

The Lock That Mimics the Pandavas

Now imagine. What if Draupadi had been born a padlock? The fact would hardly call for a leap of logic to deduce that just as it took all the five Pandavas to meet Draupadi's expectations in matrimony, it would take five keys to open such a padlock. Just as the five husbands of Draupadi represented one meta-spouse, the five keys of this lock represent one meta-key.

Fortunately, one need not imagine all of that because such a lock actually exists, and looks as shown in Figure 1a.

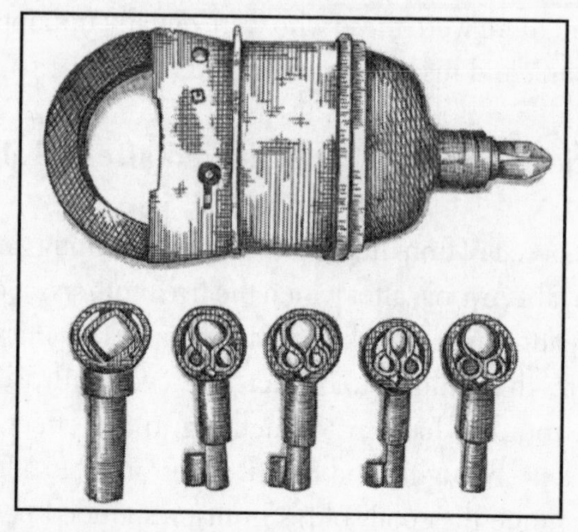

Figure 1a A lock with five keys; an old lock from Rajasthan, this design continues to be copied today for tourists (18 × 7.5 × 5 cms)

This lock seems to have been rather common in Rajasthan, and continues to be manufactured regularly, to be passed off as an 'antique' for visiting tourists. There is a practical utility to such locks as well. It is said that such locks were used in joint families where no one trusted anyone, where, say, five family members operated a business and none of them could be trusted to open the business premises or the locker unless all five members were present with their keys! In short, the lock was the key to the problem of distrust among the members of the family. It is to be expected that there are similar locks with four, three and even two keys for smaller families, as we shall soon see.

Heaven Numbers

Number five suddenly seems to be a recurring theme. Five husbands and Draupadi; five keys and a lock. So it does not come as a surprise that in Chinese mathematics, numbers one to five are together called the 'heaven' numbers. The heaven numbers are linked to distinct characteristics pertaining to the five elements – wood, water, fire, metal and earth respectively. The numbers also represent 'wu xing' – a Chinese term that can describe five of anything: the five elements, five phases, five stages, five agents, five colours, five movements or five ethics.

Five Simultaneous Equations and Draupadi's Favourite Husband

Poring over various versions of the Mahabharata, scholars have wondered, and some have tried to explore if Draupadi had any favourites among her husbands. Yudhisthira was the most upright; Bhima the most powerfully built, devoted and passionate; Arjuna was the one who actually won her hand and was the best at archery; Nakula the handsomest; Sahadeva the most scholarly. So, surely, though she had wished in her previous life to have all the five qualities in her husband, when actually faced with five husbands, each possessing one of the qualities, she could have had her preferences among them? Could the husbands have had their differences and jealousies over her? Alas, we shall never know, since the epic itself is silent on these questions of considerable gossip value.

However, the epic tells us that, duly warned by the wandering sage Narada – who minded everybody's business but his own – of the possibility of discord arising among them on account of the shared wife, the brothers worked out a Standard Operating Procedure (SOP) for time-sharing with Draupadi. Under the SOP, each brother would have exclusive access to Draupadi, one year at a time. In the chambers, the coital couple will be undisturbed by the other brothers, and the violation of this privacy would invite penance and penalty, and so forth. The epic has it that Arjuna accidentally stumbled in once when Draupadi was in the chamber with Yudhisthira and, as per the understanding among the brothers, had to proceed post-haste on pilgrimage for expiation. It is a different matter that he returned with three new wives, causing this author to wonder if his unwitting stumble was so unwitting after all!

Be that as it may, nearly 5,000 years after the epic, one is entitled not to be too delicate about the 'facts' and take some liberties in order to explore the question of Draupadi's time-sharing hypothetically, from an altogether different angle, for an altogether scholarly purpose. For instance, who can claim with certainty that Draupadi and the five brothers did not go through at least one year before the need for an SOP was felt?

Let us assume that on the first wedding anniversary, before the SOP was put in place, a long-time close friend of Draupadi asks her out of naughty friendly curiosity, which of her five husbands she favoured the most and which the least. Draupadi feigns anger at the question, but in a playful mood, tells her friend that she has a meticulous log of the number of nights she spent with each of her husbands through the year, though she has no intention of sharing the information with her! But as a tease, she is willing to share with her friend, the total number of nights spent by her with four of her husbands in five different combinations. In effect, she presents her friend with the following five equations:

$$y + b + a + n = 304$$
$$b + a + n + s = 296$$
$$a + n + s + y = 294$$
$$n + s + y + b = 280$$
$$s + y + b + a = 310$$

Where *y* stands for the total number of nights spent with Yudhisthira, *b* for the number of nights spent with Bhima, *a* for the number of nights with Arjuna, *n* for the number of nights with Nakula, and *s* for the nights spent with Sahadeva.

Draupadi tells her friend that if she can figure out who her most and least favoured husbands are using this information, she is free to draw her own conclusions!

Clearly, if Draupadi's friend wants to solve the puzzle, she needs to solve the five simultaneous equations. It is as if she has five keys with which to find her answer. Solving these five linear equations simultaneously for the value of the five unknowns should lead to the desired answer. But unless you have some familiarity with simultaneous equations, you may not make much headway. If you are a novice, for instance, you may be tempted to subtract the second equation from the first and get $y - s = 32$; subtract the third equation from the second and get $b - y = 2$; subtract the fourth equation from the third to get $a - b = 62$, and so on, and find that you aren't making much headway.

It is the same with our lock. When in a closed position, armed with all the five keys, you do not find the necessary opening (literally) to make your first move. The above set of simultaneous equations is cracked only when your first move is right, which is, for instance, to add all the five equations together, to yield:

$4y + 4b + 4a + 4n + 4s = 1{,}460;$
or,
$y + b + a + n + s = 365.$

Now subtracting each of the five simultaneous equations from the above equation, it can be easily figured that:

$s = 61, y = 69, b = 71, a = 85$ and $n = 55.$

Remember that *y*, *b*, *a*, *n* and *s* stand respectively for the total number of nights spent by Draupadi with Yudhisthira, Bhima, Arjuna, Nakula and Sahadeva. Clearly, Arjuna is the one she presumably favoured most and Nakula the least, at least in the first year of her marriage – at least under the above set of assumptions.

You notice that unless you get on to the first move, the remaining ones aren't so obvious. So what is the first move to open our lock that would enable the remaining keys to perform their designated task? To reveal the first keyhole! You need to identify the key whose handle presents the appropriate spanner (spanner-headed key) which removes the pointy tip of the lock to reveal the concealed first keyhole at the bottom. The same key is then inserted into this revealed keyhole and turned several times to reveal the remaining keyholes into which the other four keys are inserted and turned to unlock the lock. Once you have figured out the first step, the rest of the steps become apparent quite readily.

As you can see, Figure 1b explains the first step, which is to identify the correct key to unscrew the pointy tip. Once the first keyhole is exposed, the same key that unscrewed the tip is turned repeatedly so that the casing slides down, revealing four more keyholes, which is also seen in Figure 1b. When all the five keys are in place, the lock looks as shown in Figure 1c and the shackle of the lock opens.

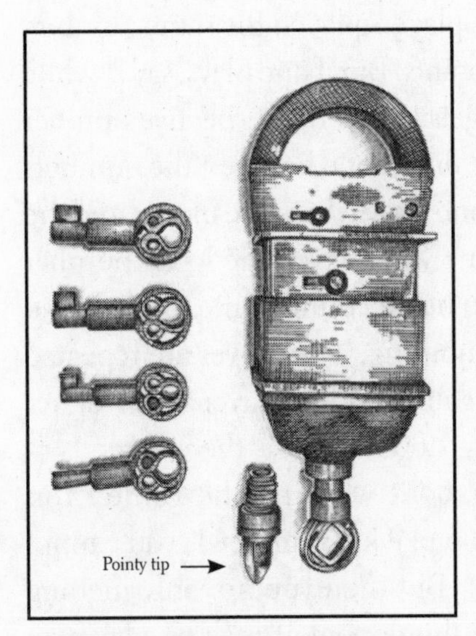

Figure 1b When this key is turned repeatedly, the casing slides down revealing four more keyholes

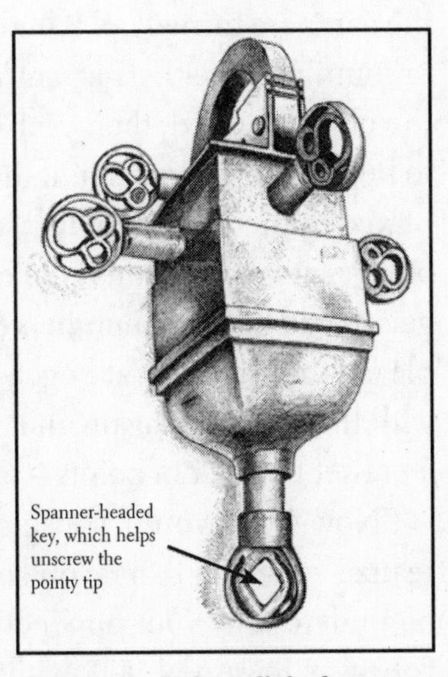

Figure 1c When all the keys are turned in place, the shackle opens

Undercut and Five Simultaneous Equations Again

Recently, while teaching behavioural economics at the University of Bocconi in Milan, I encountered an old game created by Douglas Hofstadter in his idle time, called Undercut.[1] The game, in a simplistic way, mimics the behaviour of two competitors engaged in a price war.

It goes thus: two players are dealt five cards each, each set of cards being the ace (representing the number 1), 2, 3, 4 and 5. Each holds the five cards (now representing numbers 1 to 5), face inwards, so that the numbers are concealed from the opponent. Now each player plays one of the five cards, face down. Next, both the cards are turned up. If both players played the same number, say number 4, neither gets any points. But if one plays, say 2, while the other plays a 4, then each gets to add her respective number to her account. However, if the difference between the numbers played by them differs only by one – say when one plays 2 and the other plays 3 or 1 – then the one who played the lower number gets to add both the numbers to her account, while the one who played the larger number gets nothing. The moves are repeated with the five cards again and again, and the player who reaches a pre-set number of points – say 1,000 – first, is the winner.

Now how would you go about winning the game? You realize very soon that if you keep playing number 1, you cannot be undercut by your opponent. But then you are only inching your way towards 1,000, while the opponent may be playing a series of 5s, galloping away to the winning post. If the opponent is playing 5s again and again, you realize quickly that you can take your opponent by surprise, by playing a 4, and pocket nine points. But then your opponent will expect this and would have been watching you carefully. So she entices you with a series of 5s and just when you are ready to play a four, she undercuts you with a 3, pocketing seven points! In short, the game is fiercely competitive and each opponent is trying to guess what the other is going to play and strategize accordingly. Soon, you are trying to gauge what your opponent thinks you are thinking, and so on. Does the game offer a winning strategy for either player?

Intuitively it should be obvious that the game is a symmetric one and offers no specific advantage to either player. Then perhaps it cannot offer a clear winning strategy, because if such a strategy exists, before long, it should be obvious to the other player as well. But then there cannot be two winners! However, the game does offer an optimal strategy – a statistical one to ensure that you do not fare worse than your competitor. The strategy, according to Hofstadter, was developed by one of his graduate students named Jon Peterson. The tactic is based on the relative pay-off to each player under various scenarios. Consider the following pay-off matrix for a game between you and me.

		Me				
		1	**2**	**3**	**4**	**5**
	1	0	–3	2	3	4
	2	3	0	–5	2	3
You	**3**	–2	5	0	–7	2
	4	–3	–2	7	0	–9
	5	–4	–3	–2	9	0

Figure 2 The relative pay-off for each player (the players being you and me) under various scenarios

The numbers in the cells indicate my relative pay-off when you and I play various combinations of numbers. For example, the zero in the top-left cell indicates my relative pay-off (and yours too, for that matter) if we both played 1. The second number on the top row is –3, which represents my net loss (and your gain), if I played 2 while you played 1. Similarly, the third number on the top row, 2, represents my net gain and your loss when I play 3 and you play 1. Other numbers in the cell follow the same logic. In short, the positive numbers are my gains (and your losses) and negative numbers my losses (and your gains), the entire sum adding up to zero.

The optimal strategy worked out by Jon involves solving the following five simultaneous equations:

1. $-3b + 2c + 3d + 4e = 0$
2. $3a - 5c + 2d + 3e = 0$
3. $-2a + 5b - 7d + 2e = 0$
4. $-3a - 2b + 7c - 9e = 0$
5. $-4a - 3b - 2c + 9d = 0$

The logic of the five equations should be obvious: *a*, *b*, *c*, *d*, and *e* are the statistical weights with which any number should be played for an optimal strategy. For example, if your weights for playing 1, 2, 3, 4 and 5 are *a*, *b*, *c*, *d* and *e*, respectively, then when I choose, say 2, I expect a net pay-off of $3a + 0b - 5c + 2d + 3e$, which must equal zero (from equation 2 above) if I am to emerge no worse than you. Similarly, the other four equations represent my net pay-off when I choose 1, 3, 4 or 5.

Thus, solving the five equations simultaneously, we get the values of *a*, *b*, *c*, *d*, and *e* that satisfy all the five equations, as: a =

10, b = 26, c = 13, d = 16 and e = 1. In other words, while playing any of the numbers, a player is better off playing to no systematic strategy, except to randomly play 1 about 15 per cent of the times (= 10/66), 2 about 39.5(= 26/66), 3 about 20(= 13/66), 4 about 24 (= 16/66) and 5 about 1.5 per cent of the times (= 1/66). In the long haul, this strategy ensures that you will be more or less even on your wins and losses.

Polynomials: Quintics and Beyond

Most of us know our linear equations well – the straight lines. It was always the quirky polynomials – equations of higher order – which posed untold challenges. A polynomial could be of the second, third, fourth, fifth, or of an order as high as integers can go. A quadratic equation is a polynomial of the second order; a cubic is a polynomial of the third order; a quartic, a polynomial of the fourth order; and a quintic, one of the fifth order. To render life simpler, polynomials beyond quintics are referred to as polynomials of the sixth, seventh, eighth order, and so on.

One may choose to view a polynomial equation as a lock and all its roots as the keys that will unravel the polynomial. In mathematics, polynomials of the fifth order (quintics) and beyond have a special place. We learn in school that the number of roots of a polynomial equals the order of the polynomial. For example, a linear equation has one root or one solution. A quadratic has two; a cubic equation has three. In short, a polynomial of nth degree has n solutions or n roots.[2]

Linears and Quadratics

A linear equation – the simplest of equations – is of the form $ax + b = 0$, where x is an unknown variable and a and b are known constants. With a simple solution like $x = -\frac{b}{a}$, the equation is not unlike our ordinary everyday lock that works with a single key, and like most marriages – monogamous.

A quadratic equation, on the other hand, is an equation of the second order and a little more complex and 'interesting', like bigamy, and some locks that work with two keys! The general form of a quadratic in x is: $ax^2 + bx + c = 0$, where a, b and c are some constants – typically some numbers or fractions. The quadratic is a little complex but not all that difficult. Similarly, the locks with two keys can be a little complex to crack, but not too much. While, in general, a quadratic has two solutions, it is not uncommon for a quadratic equation to have two identical roots, like a lock with duplicate set of keys.

Padlocks requiring two different keys in day-to-day use today may be rare. But you do encounter a lock requiring two keys when you visit your bank locker, of which you possess one key and the bank manager the other; and it takes both the keys to open the locker. But in the more distant past, locks requiring two keys to open were rather commonplace. See Figure 3, for example.

Characteristically, a quadratic has two roots or solutions, given by $x = \frac{-b \pm \sqrt{b^2 - 4ac}}{2a}$. A root can be imaginary (just as much as some of the stories in the Mahabharata) when $b^2 - 4ac$ is negative. Do we have a lock with keys mimicking such a situation? We do.

Take a look at the lock in Figure 4a. It does not reveal any keyhole and its access is by no means obvious. This lock needs two

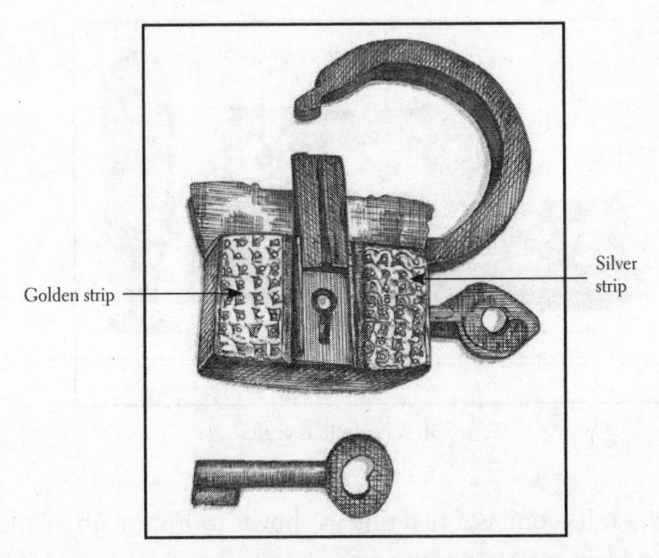

Figure 3 A lock from Rajasthan, which works with two keys; such locks are also referred to as Ganga–Jamuna, since one strip of metal on the front is golden and the other silver in colour (9.5 × 7.5 × 4 cms)

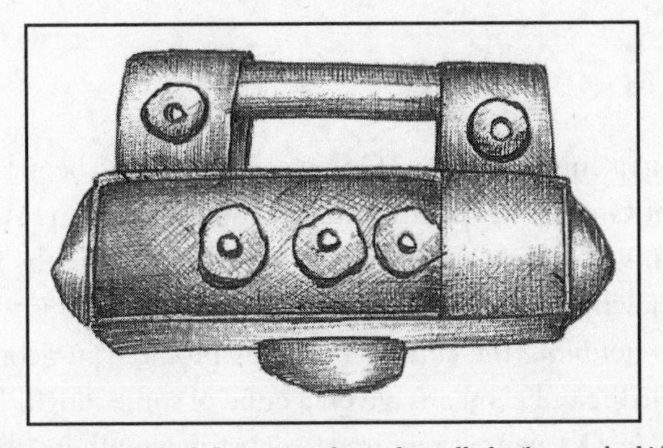

Figure 4a An old lock from Rajasthan, also called a 'battery lock' because of its resemblance to a miniature car battery when the casing is shut in place (9 × 5.5 × 2.5 cms)

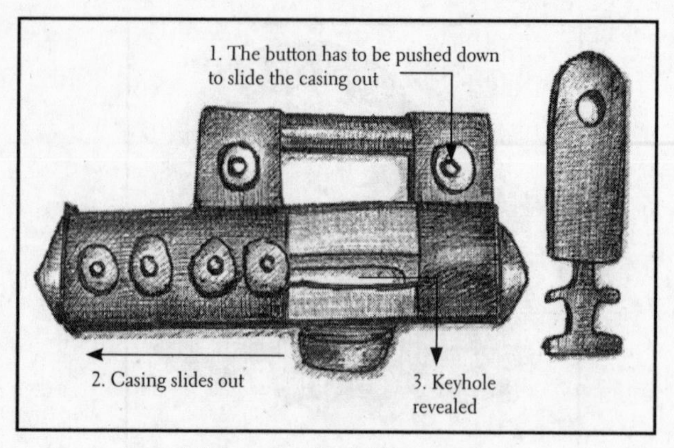

Figure 4b A keyhole revealed

keys to open it – one is a real one as shown in Figure 4b, while the second key is effectively imaginary, or a complex key which resides only in one's mind and is not real. This key comprises steps 1 and 2 shown in Figure 4b. One needs both the real and the virtual keys to open the lock.

Cubics

How about a cubic equation? Cubic equations have been known to ancient Greeks, Egyptians, Indians and Babylonians. At least some forms of cubics are known to have been solved by them. A well-known unsolvable form of the cubic problem is what is known as *doubling the cube* – a famous problem in geometry. To 'double the cube' means, given a cube of some length D and volume V (= D^3), you are required to construct another cube that has double the volume of the first (that is 2V) and has a length equal to $\sqrt[3]{2}$ D. But since the cube root of 2 is an irrational number (1.259921049…), such a construction is impossible. And that is the reason why this problem is impossible to solve using a compass and a ruler. Simply put, doubling the cube is a lock with no key!

Hippocrates was a scholar who worked on solving a cubic. In between his medical practice, Hippocrates is known to have reduced this problem to one of finding two mean proportionals (or geometric means) between one line and another twice its length. He found this problem impossible to solve using a compass and a ruler. This is hardly surprising since it simply can't be done, as this involves computing the square root of 2, which is also an irrational number (1.414213562…).

While poets are not always known for their prowess in mathematics, the Persian poet Omar Khayyam (1048–1131 AD) of *Rubaiyat* fame is reported to have made significant contributions to the field of cubic equations, and figured out that a cubic could have more than one solution. He is also said to have recognized that while a cubic cannot be solved using a compass and a ruler, geometric solutions could be found involving trigonometric tables or intersecting conic sections.

Also around the same time, Leonardo de Pisa, better known as Fibonacci (1170–1250AD), found a solution to the cubic equation $x^3 + 2x^2 + 10x = 20$, using Babylonian mathematics (using cuneiform numerals), which though ostensibly based on the decimal system, was in fact based on a sexagesimal system or a base of 60 (in place of 100).

For example, in cuneiform, the numerals were written as shown in Figure 5.

Fibonacci's answer to the cubic above was written as 1,22,7,42,33,4,40, which is equivalent to: $1 + 22/60 + 7/60^2 + 42/60^3 + 33/60^4 + 4/60^5 + 40/60^6$, which in our present system represents 1.368808108.

1	11	21	31	41	51
2	12	22	32	42	52
3	13	23	33	43	53
4	14	24	34	44	54
5	15	25	35	45	55
6	16	26	36	46	56
7	17	27	37	47	57
8	18	28	38	48	58
9	19	29	39	49	59
10	20	30	40	50	

Figure 5 Cuneiform numerals

In 1530, Niccolò Tartaglia is said to have cracked the cubic comprehensively. However, he failed to get formal recognition for his work as he did not publish his result. The credit was eventually shared by Girolamo Cardano and his protégé Lodovico Ferrari (who will be referred to again shortly), who were contemporary mathematicians, also working on solving polynomials.

The solution to the cubic or finding its roots involves expressing the roots as formulae involving simple functions like square and cube roots. Generally speaking, this leads to a closed form solution, yielding all the three roots of a cubic, even if the solution is not for the weak-hearted! But if you are keen, you may want to consult endnote 3. The solutions look as difficult as finding the three highest qualities in a single man, leave alone five!

Figures 6 to 9 represent some interesting examples of locks with three keys.

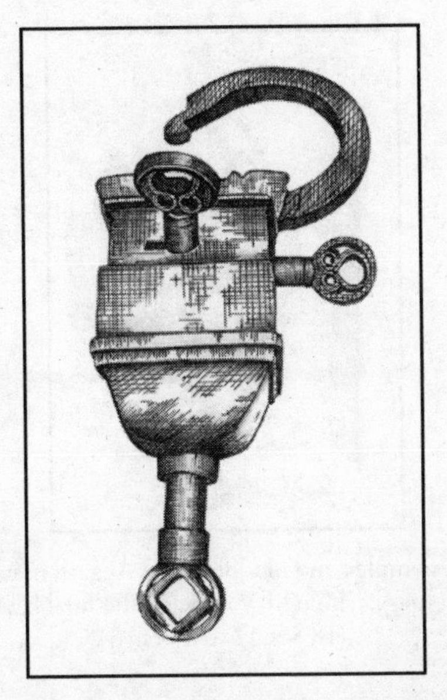

Figure 6 An ancient lock from Rajasthan, which continues to be copied today for tourists (14 × 6.5 × 4 cms)

Figure 7 A new lock copied from old designs, probably from Nepal (14 × 5.5 × 4 cms)

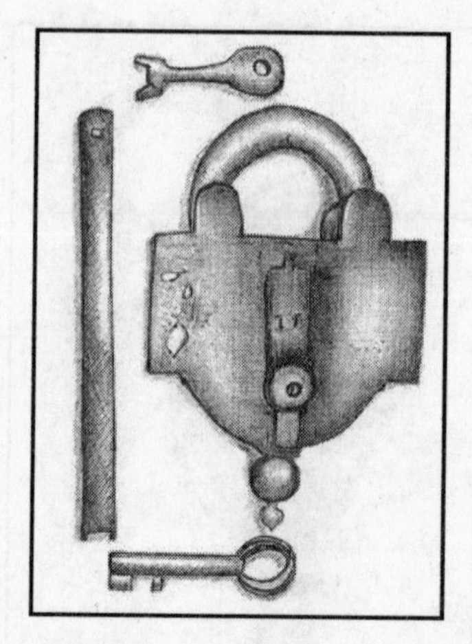

Figure 8 A very rare, complex and old lock from Aligarh in which each key leads to another keyhole till you reach the final keyhole
(18.5 × 12 × 3.5 cms)

Locks in figures 6 and 7 are relatively simple to open, just as some cubics are easy to solve. But the lock in Figure 8 above, like some obstinate cubics, is an extremely difficult one to open, involving six different steps, even when you have all the three keys.

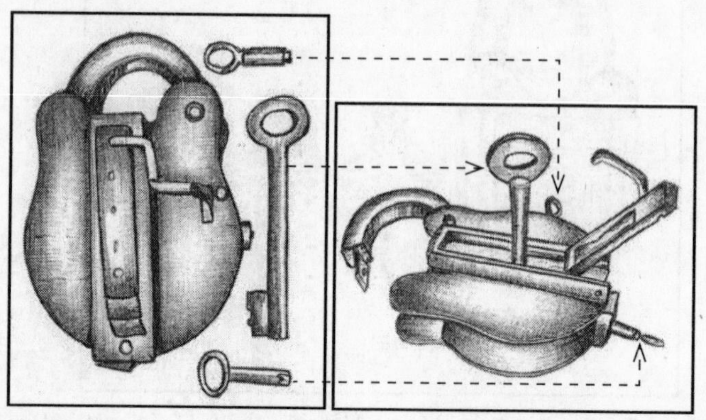

Figure 9 An old and complex lock that was used by government treasuries
(19.5 × 13 × 5.5 cms)

Figure 9 shows another example of a lock with three keys that was used by the government treasuries during the British period.

Quartics

Do all quartics have a closed-form solution? Well, they do. If you were brave enough to go to the endnote for the cubics, you would have observed that even a closed-form solution for a general cubic is certainly not a pastime for the idle. So we will spare ourselves the solution for solving an equation of the fourth order. But yes, it can be solved, horrendous though the solution may be. It is something like, if we work hard enough, we may find one man with the four highest qualities; but, boy, will we have to work hard! And that's why even showing the solution as an endnote to the general quartic is beyond the scope of this book. But if you have the heart, I suggest you check out the solution on Wikipedia.[4]

The solution has a lot of interesting stories associated with it, involving such great mathematicians as Lodovico Ferrari, Girolamo Cardano, Zuanne da Coi, Niccolò Tartaglia, Antonio Fiore, and Scipionedel Ferro. The quest for the solution to the general quartic is set in and around Venice, and is flush with every conceivable machination and intrigue. But that is a Mahabharata of a later era. However, if you do wish to go looking for Lodovico's solution to the general quartic, together with that of the cubic by his mentor Girolomo Cardano, go check out *Ars Magna* – meaning the great art – an important book on algebra authored by Cardano in 1545.

While Tartaglia's loss of credit for solving the cubics may be somewhat tragic, it was nothing compared to another tragedy surrounding the solving of quintics. It is said that in the century before, in 1486, Spanish mathematician Paolo Valmes was burnt at the stake for claiming to have solved the quartic equation, when it turned out that he had not. Inquisitor General Tomás de Torquemada is reported to have told Valmes that *it was the will of God that such a solution be inaccessible to human understanding*! He wasn't too off the mark!

Figures 10 and 11 show a couple of locks that work with four keys.

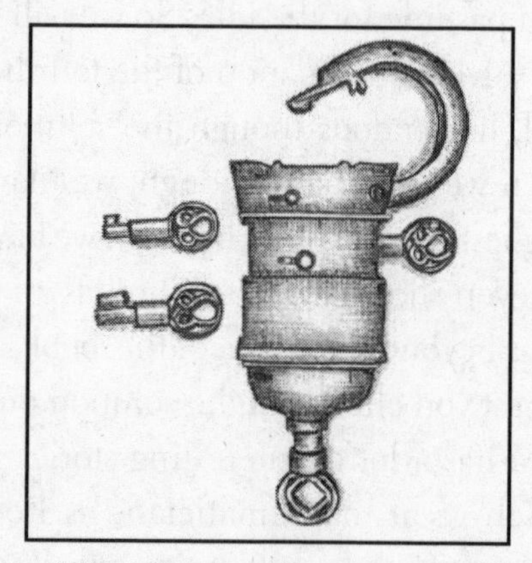

Figure 10 An old lock from Rajasthan, occasionally copied today for tourists (14 × 6.5 × 4 cms)

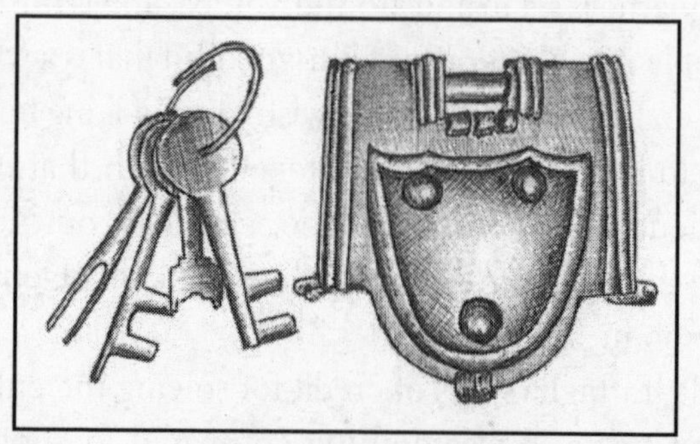

Figure 11 A very rare and complex old lock from Rajasthan/Gujarat (14.5 × 14 × 5.5 cms)

Quintics

And finally to the quintics. Typically, quadratics, cubics and quartics can be solved by factorization into radicals, even if the roots turn out to be irrational or imaginary numbers. Closed-form solutions which worked until now, no longer work for quintics (or pentics) in general. Niels Abel proved in 1824 that a quartic is the highest degree of general polynomial for which closed-form solutions can be found, though some quintics can be solved by factorizing them into radicals.

Solutions (that is, computing all the five roots) to the general quintic equations may be given in terms of Jacobi theta or hypergeometric functions (don't even try to worry about what they are) in a single variable – like putting the five highest qualities in a single man. While there may be some quintics that may be solved, albeit not without some serious mathematical acrobatics, there are many that cannot be solved at all. For example, $x^5 - x - 1 = 0$. Try it, if you don't believe me. That's like a lock with five keyholes for which keys don't exist! In practice, quintics and higher-order polynomials are solved using iterative approximations or computerized exhaustive enumeration, which is like blasting a lock open since you can't pick it, or shooting your husband because you can't find the five highest qualities in him.

Perhaps our gods understood rightly that to find all five high qualities in a single husband was as impossible as finding a closed-form solution to a quintic. Perhaps that's why locks with more than five keys are truly rare as well.

TWO

JARASANDHA, THE SPLIT LOCK AND SYMMETRIES

Foundations of Indraprastha

With Arjuna in the guise of an unlikely Brahmin winning Draupadi's hand, the Pandavas' cover was blown. So the five brothers, with their newly-wed wife, decided to return to Hastinapura openly to lay claim to their share of the kingdom. Duryodhana, reeling from the inexplicable escape of the Pandavas from his carefully laid trap, was in no frame of mind to accept any proposition that would give away any part of the thriving kingdom to his five abominable – and now seemingly fire-proof – cousins. While the visually challenged King Dhritarashtra wasn't averse to settling the matter peaceably, Duryodhana was staunchly opposed to the idea. Nevertheless, Dhritarashtra split the kingdom into two halves in an effort to bring about peace between his jealous sons and the self-righteous Pandavas. To the fact that the half granted to the Pandavas comprised mostly wild and forested land, the old king turned a blind eye (no pun intended, mind you). This cunningness on part of the old patriarch was much appreciated by his five-score sons.

The Pandavas, by dint of their industry and imagination – all the more honed by their constant wandering and hardships while legging it through forest after forest – and with some help from Vishwakarma, the architect of the gods, succeeded in building a prosperous empire, with Indraprastha as the capital. They consolidated their kingdom rapidly, built fabulous palaces and gardens, and the populace was happy, prosperous and satisfied, not unlike the opening scenes of the Gaul Village in Asterix comics.

As Indraprastha prospered, so did the might of the Pandavas. Hastinapura saw a mass exodus of skilled artists and artisans moving to the neighbouring kingdom, thanks to the double-digit growth in the GDP in the newly founded city. Soon, it was obvious that the Pandavas ruled over a kingdom that surpassed any other in Bharatavarsha in economic and military might. It was becoming evident that the Pandavas will soon be formalizing their newly acquired status. This stoked the old hatred in the depths of Duryodhana's insecure and gloomy heart.

So, before long, Bhima and Arjuna – the most martially inclined of the five brothers – began to lean on Yudhisthira to perform rajasuya, a coronation ceremony that would underscore Yudhisthira's supremacy as the potentate or the emperor of emperors. The rajasuya would consolidate their power and for good measure show their cousins, the Kauravas, their proper station in life. Bhima and Arjuna convinced a reluctant and pacifist Yudhisthira that it was the duty of kings to expand their kingdoms, and that if kingdoms did not grow, they were bound to shrink in stature and also liable to be overtaken and consequently taken over by others. You either establish your superiority over the lesser states, or *they* establish their superiority over *you* – talk familiar in the corporate merger-acquisition lore today.

Jarasandha: The Fly in the Ointment

But if the plan was to be rolled out, there seemed to be that proverbial fly in the ointment: Jarasandha, the ruler of mighty

Magadha – the empire encompassing eastern India, with its epicentre in present-day Bihar – who could be trusted to oppose Yudhisthira's hegemony. A mighty and unconquered king, Jarasandha ruled like a time-tested overlord. His prisons were supposed to be overflowing with hundreds of lesser rulers and he was widely regarded as unjust and cruel. Even if mighty warriors like Duryodhana, Shishupala and even Karna accepted Yudhisthira as the uncontested emperor, Jarasandha would certainly not. Enter wily Krishna, the friend of the Pandavas; also a relative. As on several other occasions, he rendered clever but dubious advice to defeat and kill Jarasandha who was, as of then, just minding his own business. Krishna was categorical that only Jarasandha's death could enable Yudhisthira to undertake the rajasuya successfully. While the amiable Yudhisthira ostensibly abhorred the idea of murdering someone for personal glory, he allowed himself to be prevailed upon by Lord Krishna as well as the pugnacious duo of Bhima and Arjuna, who never let him forget that the highest virtue of Kshatriya kings was ambition and their highest duty, the expansion of their kingdoms. That Jarasandha was considered unjust and ruthless was somehow taken as a justification for the action. In recent years, George Bush's waging of war on Saddam Hussein's Iraq had a similar ring to it.

Ergo, the Pandavas decided that Jarasandha had to be slain. However, the story of his slaying will be relevant to the narrative of our locks only if we are acquainted with Jarasandha's backstory.

Brihadratha: The Childless Ruler of Magadha

Brihadratha was a mighty ruler of Magadha, married to the twin daughters of the ruler of Kashi. But he was, alas, not blessed with a child. This was a source of great melancholy for the king and his queens alike. So distraught was he that he entrusted his kingdom to his ministers and, accompanied by his two wives, departed for the forest to practise severe austerities, which in those days was considered a sure recipe to beget offspring. In the course of his wanderings, he sought out the great Sage Kaushika to offer him his respects. Paying homage to learned men was a royal custom, and a beneficial one at that, given that sages in those days not only enquired after one's deeply held desires as one took leave, but had the power to grant them as well! Sure enough, when respects had been paid and accepted, and the king sought to take the learned man's leave from under the mango tree where he sat in padmasana, the sage called upon the king to state his wish. Upon hearing of the sovereign's longing for a child, the sage was still figuring out the best possible way to help him, IVF being unknown those days, when a ripe mango fell into the sage's lap.

He held the mango in his palm and extended it towards the king and spake thus: 'O king! Have either of your wives consume this humble fruit, and she shall bear you the fruit you seek – the child you crave!' The king accepted the fruit with gratitude and took leave with a spring in his step.

However, the good king had vowed never to favour one wife over the other – a wise resolution, no doubt. So he did the logical thing and cut the fruit into two halves and gave one half to each of his wives. He had not accounted for the uncommon ways of the sages, whose wordings of wishes granted often navigated paths more labyrinthine than the Anglo-Saxon legal system of today.

Two Half-babies and How They Made a Full Baby

In due course, the two wives became pregnant, but what followed wasn't half expected. Each wife gave birth to one half of a child – the left part being borne by one and the right one by the other. So, instead of one beautiful child, the king had two symmetrical half-babies. The king, muttering under his breath at these too-smart-by-the-half sages with their half-baked boons, left his lunch halfway, having lost his appetite, and ordered his staff to dispose of the two half-monsters within half an hour.

The staff did what many in this country continue to do even today, and simply dumped the masses of flesh in the nearest garbage heap, hoping Mother Nature, or whatever gods are in charge of garbage, would take care of the rest. Well, this time around, Mother Nature came in the garb of a female demon (a raakshasi) who was foraging for a meal in the vicinity.

A methodical demoness, the raakshasi laid the two halves side by side in order to consume them one after the other. But no sooner did she do so, they miraculously joined together to form a beautiful baby! Whether the raakshasi was a woman tender of heart, or the shock of seeing the two lumps of flesh come together into a beautiful baby somewhat addled her brain, we will never know. But seeing the beautiful baby, the raakshasi lost her appetite and, having got wind of the king's tragic story, restored the baby to a grateful king. The baby was, of course, Jarasandha, who grew up with exceptional looks and strength, as may be expected of a child born of divine intervention.

Thus, Jarasandha was a man made of two halves and, for that reason, could be split asunder; but if laid side by side in the correct left and right juxtaposition, he could come alive and be fully functional in no time at all!

Slaying of Jarasandha

It is this mighty Jarasandha whom Bhima, Arjuna and Krishna set out to slay. They gained entry into the Magadhan palace by subterfuge, dressed in the garb of learned religious men, because Jarasandha was known to never turn away itinerant scholars without offering them his courtesies and hospitality. Ever gracious to such men, Jarasandha offered to meet them at their convenience, rather than his own. Aware of the king's benevolence in this regard, our disguised assassins sought an appointment with the king at midnight, at which time they hoped to carry out their dark deed quietly. No nincompoop, Jarasandha grew suspicious of this unusual request and challenged them to reveal their identity. The trio did so. But with their cover blown, they offered to fight him one on one, giving him the choice of any one of them to fight with. The valiant, if aging, Jarasandha chose to fight Bhima – an extremely well-built man in the prime of his youth – as his equal, dismissing Krishna as a cowherd and Arjuna as a mere lad.

The two warriors being well matched, the fight went on for two weeks, with no result in sight. At last, on the fourteenth day, Bhima tore Jarasandha asunder and threw the two pieces away. No sooner did he do so, the two halves joined again to make a whole Jarasandha, who fought Bhima with even greater vigour and valour. Every time Bhima managed to tear Jarasandha into two, the halves of the Magadhan king would come back together, leaving Bhima frustrated and exhausted. Krishna, the sneaky strategist, forbidden from any direct intervention in the fight, casually picked up a straw, split it through the middle, and threw the halves across each other – that is, the left piece to the right and vice versa.

Bhima, though usually regarded more for his brawn than his brain, got the clue nevertheless, and as he tore Jarasandha into two the next time, he threw the two pieces in opposite directions, so that the halves could not rejoin. And thus was Jarasandha slain, paving the way for the rajasuya.

A Lock Made of Two Halves

Now why am I narrating this story? To show you a lock that is not unlike Jarasandha, in the sense that two halves of this lock come together to make a whole! Take a look at Figure 12a.

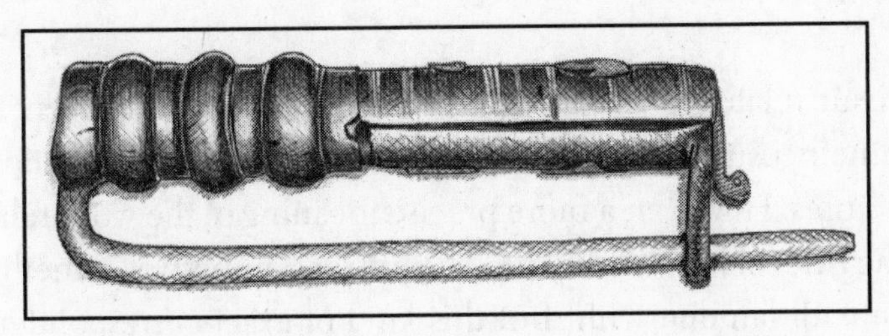

Figure 12a An unusual cylindrical lock which roughly divides into two equal halves when opened (28 × 8 × 5 cms)

Like Jarasandha, the halves join to make the lock whole only when juxtaposed right. Or they remain useless! Also like Jarasandha, if the lock is to be opened, the key must pry the two halves apart. See figures 12b and 12c to see how the two halves come apart.

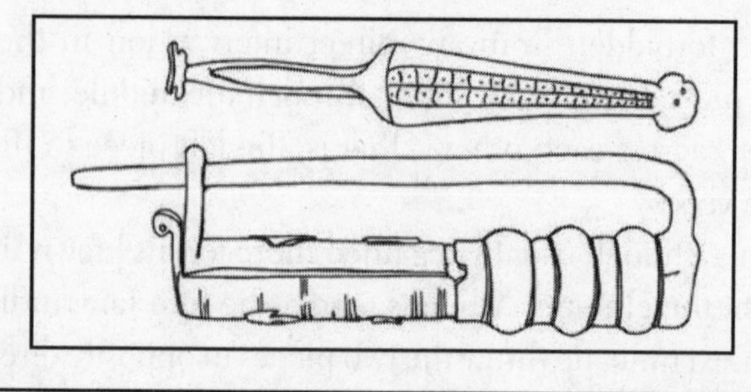

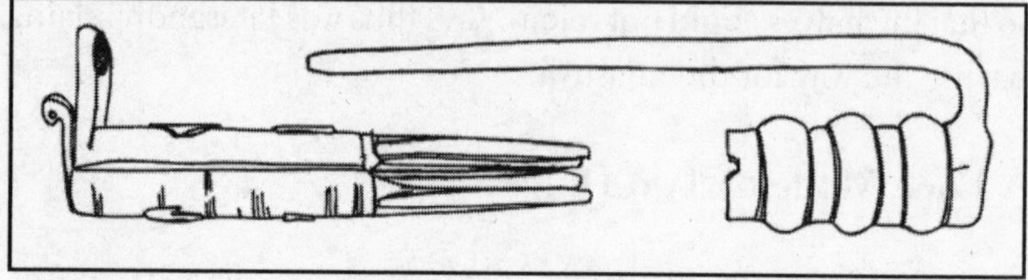

Figures 12b and 12c The two halves of the lock shown in closed and open positions; the key is shown above the lock in Figure 10 a

Symmetry

An issue related to Jarasandha is symmetry. A casual reference to symmetry usually makes one think of harmony and aesthetics in structures. However, a more precise meaning of the word relates to the rules of formal systems. The mirror symmetry is something we are all familiar with. But this kind of exact correspondence is common among most living beings, including humans. For example, if you drew a line from the top of Jarasandha's head to the crotch, his body would be identical on both the sides. Leonardo da Vinci shows such symmetry in his famous drawing *The Vitruvian Man* (see Figure 13, which is a modified version of the original drawing of da Vinci).

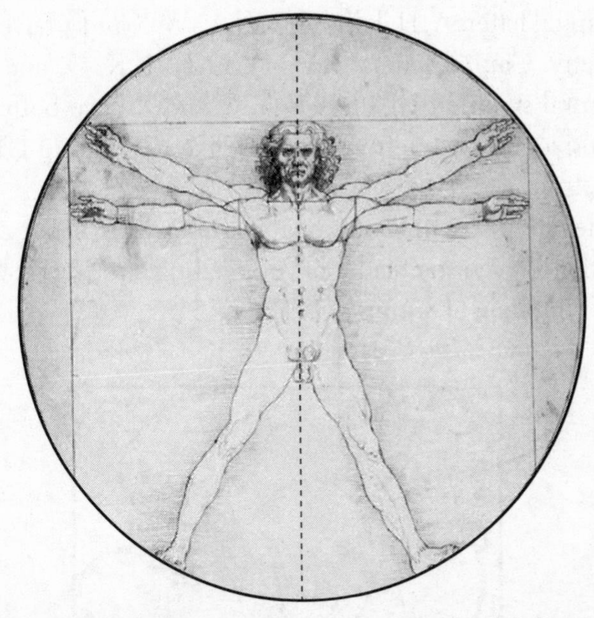

Figure 13 Leonardo da Vinci's *The Vitruvian Man* (modified image)

Again, while human forms may have a vertical line of symmetry, others may have a plane of symmetry. For example, when you slice an apple through the middle, you have two halves on either side of a plane of symmetry. Even mirror or reflection symmetry may correspond to both line and plane of symmetry. Forms, like a circle or sphere, may have infinite lines or planes of symmetries – any diameter or a plane of diameter being a line or plane of symmetry. Much of such obvious exact correspondences in the universe is encountered in the geometry of forms. That's why there are many types of symmetries. Many of these can be observed in works of art (say in the Jain cosmology) and architecture (say in Taj Mahal).

Capital letters A, H, I, M, O, T, U, V, W, X and Y have vertical symmetry. Capital letters B, C, D, E, H, I, K, O, and X have horizontal symmetry. Letters H, I, O and X have both vertical and horizontal symmetry. Alphabets like F, G, J and L have no symmetry.

Then there is the rotational symmetry, as in an aircraft's propeller or even the blades of your ceiling fan (Figure14). And there is the helical symmetry (Figure 15).

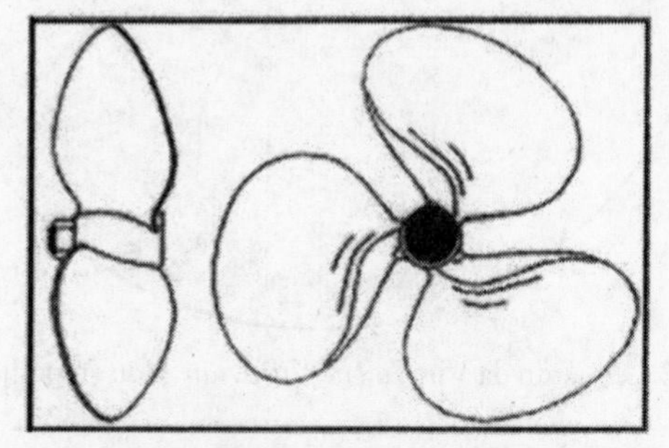

Figure 14 Rotational symmetry

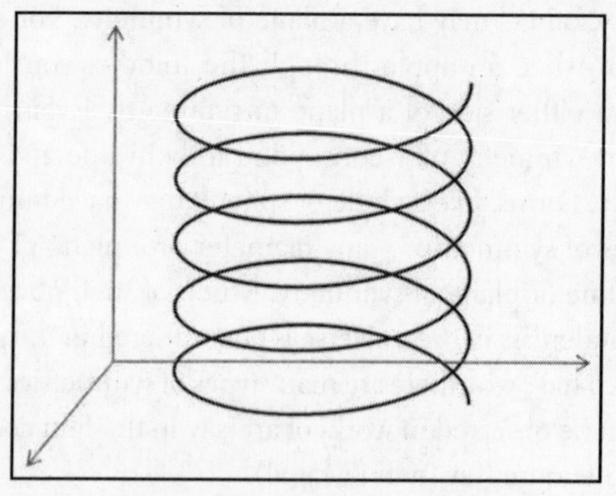

Figure 15 Spiral or helical symmetry

There is the inverted symmetry, for example, in the upside-down image of an object one sees through a convex lens. Such symmetry is obtained only when we track the path of the light rays refracted through a convex lens and observe that the image is reversed not just horizontally, but vertically as well – in other words, the inverted image is a 180-degree rotation about the axis, passing through the centre of the lens. In a sine curve, the first half is symmetrical to the second with 180-degree flip. With a Mobius strip, we have a transformational symmetry, while Pretzel knots have a twisting one.

While most conventional locks are vertically symmetric through their middle, figures 16, 17 and 18 present some interesting examples.

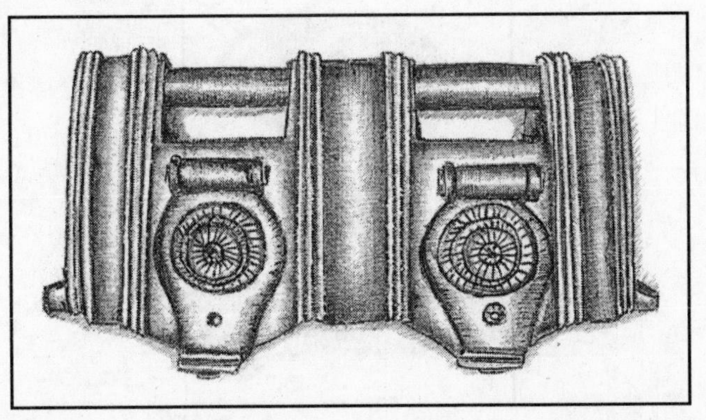

Figure 16 An unusual lock with two shackles, with artistic symmetry (22 × 11 ×7 cms)

The unusual symmetrical locks with twin shackles in figures 16 and 17 are for specially designed door bolts. In the lock shown in Figure 16, for instance, each side presents just one half of the lock. It is only when you work both the halves that the lock is opened or closed.

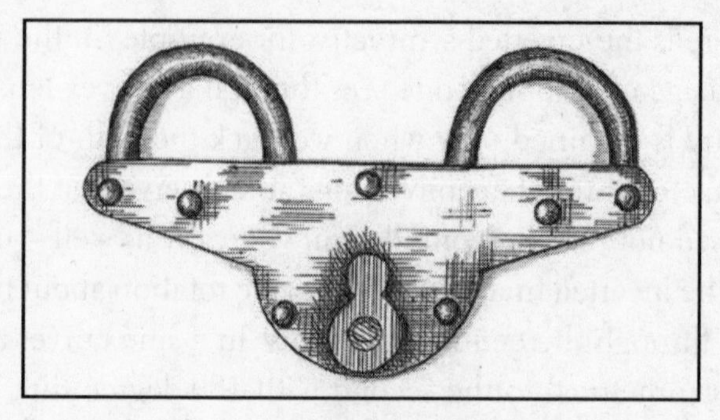

Figure 17 An unusual lock with two shackles, with simple symmetry (20 × 11.5 × 3 cms)

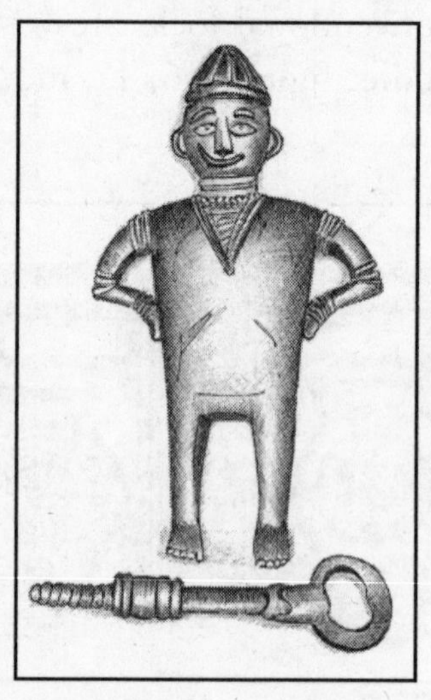

Figure 18 Parsi man, probably from Aligarh, arms akimbo; the shackle is at the back (12.5 × 7 × 5 cms)

Symmetry of Binomial Coefficients

Symmetry may also be present in the form of coefficients of equations – in binomial coefficients (discussed in more detail in Chapter 3), for instance. Here are a few examples:

$$(a+b)^0 = 1$$
$$(a+b)^1 = a + b$$
$$(a+b)^2 = a^2 + 2ab + b^2$$
$$(a+b)^3 = a^3 + 3a^2b + 3ab^2 + b^3$$
$$(a+b)^4 = a^4 + 4a^3b + 6a^2b^2 + 4ab^3 + b^4$$
$$(a+b)^5 = a^5 + 5a^4b + 10a^3b^2 + 10a^2b^3 + 5ab^4 + b^5$$
$$(a+b)^6 = a^6 + 6a^5b + 15a^4b^2 + 20a^3b^3 + 15a^2b^4 + 6ab^5 + b^6$$

The sequence of coefficients would look like this:

n													
0							1						
1						1		1					
2					1		2		1				
3				1		3		3		1			
4			1		4		6		4		1		
5		1		5		10		10		5		1	
6	1		6		15		20		15		6		1

The inherent mirroring across a vertical line of symmetry through the middle of the triangle is obvious. The left half of what is called the Pascal's triangle overlaps exactly with the right half along the vertical central 'line'. So useful is the property of symmetry in equations that by classifying the symmetry of polynomial equations using the instrument of group theory, one may prove why quintic equations – that is equations of the kind $(a + b)^5$ and higher powers – are not solvable.

Simple Arithmetic Symmetries

And here are a few more well-known, but more interesting symmetric arithmetic formulations:

$$1 \times 8 + 1 = 9$$
$$12 \times 8 + 2 = 98$$
$$123 \times 8 + 3 = 987$$
$$1234 \times 8 + 4 = 9876$$
$$12345 \times 8 + 5 = 98765$$
$$123456 \times 8 + 6 = 987654$$
$$1234567 \times 8 + 7 = 9876543$$
$$12345678 \times 8 + 8 = 98765432$$
$$123456789 \times 8 + 9 = 987654321$$

and

$$1 \times 9 + 2 = 11$$
$$12 \times 9 + 3 = 111$$
$$123 \times 9 + 4 = 1111$$
$$1234 \times 9 + 5 = 11111$$
$$12345 \times 9 + 6 = 111111$$
$$123456 \times 9 + 7 = 1111111$$
$$1234567 \times 9 + 8 = 11111111$$
$$12345678 \times 9 + 9 = 111111111$$
$$123456789 \times 9 + 10 = 1111111111$$

and

$$9 \times 9 + 7 = 88$$
$$98 \times 9 + 6 = 888$$
$$987 \times 9 + 5 = 8888$$
$$9876 \times 9 + 4 = 88888$$
$$98765 \times 9 + 3 = 888888$$
$$987654 \times 9 + 2 = 8888888$$
$$9876543 \times 9 + 1 = 88888888$$
$$98765432 \times 9 + 0 = 888888888$$

and

$$1 \times 1 = 1$$
$$11 \times 11 = 121$$
$$111 \times 111 = 12321$$
$$1111 \times 1111 = 1234321$$
$$11111 \times 11111 = 123454321$$
$$111111 \times 111111 = 12345654321$$
$$1111111 \times 1111111 = 1234567654321$$
$$11111111 \times 11111111 = 123456787654321$$
$$111111111 \times 111111111 = 123456789\ 87654321$$

Nature itself is full of symmetries. Bilateral symmetry – the splitting into two equal halves so that one part is a mirror image of the other – is inherent to the taxonomy of most animals. The butterfly is one example (Figure 19). But so are most moths, insects, human face and any number of other animals, fish and birds. Many animals also exhibit radial, spiral or other forms of symmetries.

Figure 19 A symmetrical butterfly

Symmetry plays a major role in physics as well. For instance, the Noether's theorem of symmetry states that each symmetry of a system leads to a physically conserved quantity – that time translation symmetry leads to conservation of energy; space translation symmetry to conservation of momentum; rotational symmetry yields conservation of angular momentum; and so forth.

So it is safe to say that symmetry plays a role in the universe, including in mathematics, the Mahabharata, and man-made objects such as locks.

THREE

THE ILLUSORY PALACE, INVISIBLE KEYHOLES AND ELUSIVE CODES

The Rajasuya Yajna

With Jarasandha out of the way, the coast was clear for Yudhisthira to proceed with the preparations for the rajasuya yajna. Invitations were soon couriered all around to various kingdoms, including the Kauravas, for the forthcoming event. The yajna, announcing the 'arrival' of the Pandavas, was no music to Duryodhana's ears. Understandably, he was in no mood to attend the yajna, which implied acceptance of the domination of Pandavas – the very cousins he had loved to loathe for as long as he could remember. And yet, the only honourable way of not attending the event would be to challenge the dominant status of the Pandavas and defeating them in an open war or duel. And this, he and his allies were in no position to do, especially since the chilling killing of the wily Jarasandha was still fresh in his memory. Besides, old man Dhritarashtra, guru Drona, grand sire Bhishma, and everyone else who had a long, grey beard seemed to be advising him but one thing – that he gulp down the bitter aftertaste of the Pandavas' success and attend the event.

The Illusory Palace and Duryodhana's Humiliation

In the meantime, the Pandavas had resolved that some extravaganza on the occasion of the rajasuya would not be entirely misplaced. They decided to put up a show that would dazzle and daze, as well as awe and astound all those who attended the mighty spectacle.

Accordingly, Yudhisthira appointed the services of Maya, the artificer or architect of the asuras (just as Vishwakarma was the architect of the gods), to build the assembly palace where the rajasuya was to be performed. Maya – which means illusion, by the way – living up to his name, created a palace like no other, complete with optical illusions where solid floors appeared like pools of water and vice versa. The walls were painted like most realistic doors, while doors gave the impression of being solid walls, and so forth, not to speak of the liberal use of golden paint and ruby studded alcoves and mother-of-pearl furniture. Basically, the works.

The guests were beginning to saunter in. There wasn't one among them who did not stand captivated by the sheer magnificence of the palace, breath on hold. They stood dazed – the very effect the palace was expected to have on a visitor – at the shine, sparkle, glint and gleam of the ambience. The situation got trickier as the visitors struggled to cope with the illusions, laboriously put in place by Maya for that very purpose.

Draupadi, it would seem, was amusing herself seated behind a screen along with her friends, spying on the guests struggling with the illusions.

It was then that a surly Duryodhana with a throbbing head (thanks to the aforementioned jealousy) swaggered into the venue, trying to look oblivious to the grandeur of the palace. But the illusions were another thing. They were no respecters of one's moods or background.

Much to Draupadi's amusement, he came, he saw and he walked onto what he thought was a carpet of flowers laid out for his welcome. And before you could say Dury..., he was gasping for breath in a pool of water, with his crown lost in the process, and water dripping from every pore of his body. Quite excited by now, Draupadi was even more amused when, while wading out of the water, he tried to hurriedly enter an adjacent room to organize himself, only to bang his head against what he thought was an open door, but was a painted wall. The net result of all this amusement was that Draupadi burst out giggling, loudly and noticeably.

True, Duryodhana cut less than a debonair figure. A more chivalrous man might have sheepishly grinned at the beautiful princess and moved on. But either Duryodhana was less than chivalrous, or Draupadi's giggle was more a derisive snigger, and Duryodhana understandably took umbrage.

That the insult had been meted out by a woman whom he had once desired, and who was now married to his most hated rivals, that too at a time when he was still smarting from the humiliation of having to attend a hated cousin's rajasuya, hardly added to Duryodhana's cheer. He glared at Draupadi in silence and vowed to avenge the insult that had been added to injury.

A Lock Full of Illusions

Had Maya thought of this lock, he might well have considered hanging one on the bolts of the doors on the guests' rooms.

It might have added to Draupadi's mirth to see a baffled Duryodhana, key in hand, fiddle with the lock forever and get nowhere, the apparent keyhole not being a keyhole at all! But no, Maya created no such lock.

But some locksmiths from a bygone generation in Uttar Pradesh, Rajasthan, and Gujarat did. The lock you see in Figure 20a seems of the innocuous, run-of-the-mill variety. The keyhole is clearly visible, and the key fits snugly into it, as it is expected to. But you may keep turning the key to no avail for the simple reason that the keyhole you see is not the real keyhole at all, but just a red herring! The real keyhole is concealed in the lock! How do you conceal a keyhole? Take a look at the image. You could hardly blame Duryodhana if he took it for just another lock and tried to turn the key in the obvious keyhole furiously.

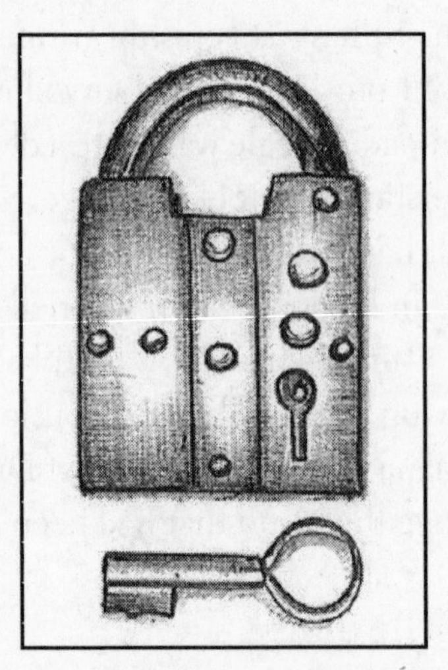

Figure 20a A simple trick lock, with origins in Aligarh ($8 \times 5.5 \times 2$ cms)

So where is the keyhole concealed? It sounds simple when the answer is provided pat. But people usually flounder for quite some time before giving up in disgust.

The true keyhole lies under the vertical band which seems tightly attached to the body of the lock for strength, but is riveted only on one end and turns on its lower axis, revealing the real keyhole as shown in Figure 20b.

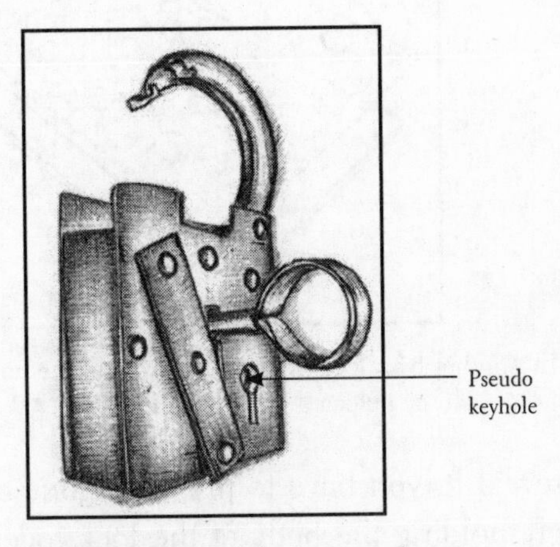

Figure 20b The trick lock, opened

The lock is designed to fool you only once. That's why there are as many variations to the illusory keyhole theme as there are locksmiths. Basically, what these locks try to do is what in computer science is called steganography – the science of hiding information. These locks try to hide the information on the keyhole, just as Maya's palace was trying to hide the pool Duryodhana fell into. But if you look closely, the same lock also contains elements of cryptography, whose objective is to make data incomprehensible to the third party. So, though the vertical strip is there for all to see, the real keyhole is well concealed from the observer's eyes.

Figure 21a is another example of a similar lock, with elements of both steganography and cryptography. No matter from which direction you check out the lock, one is unable to locate a keyhole. Figure 21a shows the lock from one angle. The sides hidden from view do not show any sign of a keyhole either.

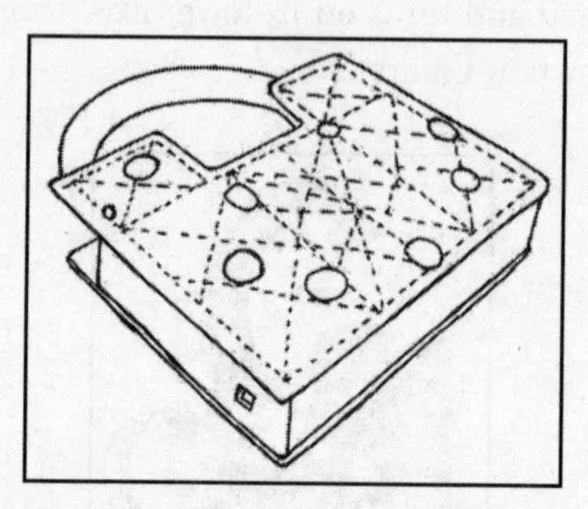

Figure 21a Another trick lock, more complex than the previous one; no keyhole can be detected anywhere (15 × 11.5 × 2.5 cms)

To reveal it, you have to pry under one of the many rivets seemingly holding the body of the lock together. A lid hiding the keyhole snaps open (see below). Here you have the art of cryptography in all its glory.

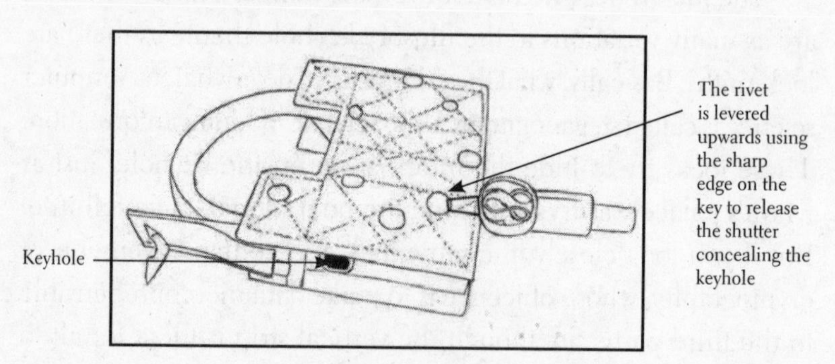

Figure 21b The keyhole, revealed

Figure 21c The lock in open position

Applying the key to the revealed keyhole opens the lock, as shown in Figure 21c.

The Camp with the Security Code

Now imagine a spy wishing to enter an army unit that uses a certain code to allow entry to its soldiers. The spy could well be a disguised Duryodhana trying to get into the Pandava camp. From his vitae, it would seem that it wouldn't be beyond him to think of engineering a surreptitious entry into the rival camp. So let us say he secretly watches and listens in on those entering the camp. As the first soldier strolls into the camp, the guard at the gates says, '12' and the soldier responds with '6'. Another soldier walks up, the guard says, '6', and the soldier replies '3'. A smile crosses Duryodhana's lips. He confidently walks up to the enemy gates and when the sentry says '10', our trespasser says '5'. The guard stops Duryodhana for the impostor that he is. Why?

Why couldn't Duryodhana open the lock, or enter the Pandava camp? For the same reason he fell into the pool of water at the rajasuya venue. In each of these three situations, what you see is not what you get. If it was an illusion of a floor that got him into deep waters (and no pun intended) at the rajasuya venue, it would be an illusory keyhole that would prevent him from opening the lock, and now, it is the illusory code that thwarts his attempts to enter the camp.

The code is apparently easily cracked – half the number quoted by the watchman. But that's what leads Duryodhana astray because what meets the eye is an illusion.

What's the real coding scheme? In this case, it was the number of letters which spells the number. The word 'twelve' has six letters in it; 'six' has three. And so the response or the correct key to 'ten' should have been 'three'. The code could well have been double the number of letter or square of the number of letters, etc.

The fact is that the camp may be coded with virtually any kind of scheme, series or function, so that entry into the camp would call for cracking the scheme, series or the function. As long as we decipher the code properly, we have the key.

For example, the function embedded in the code may be a simple linear one, such as $y = ax + b$, or a higher-order polynomial like $y = ax^4 + bx^3 + cx^2 + dx + e$, with the value of the constants, a, b, c, d, etc., known beforehand.

As long as we know the function, and till the time we are required to supply y in response to the guard's x, it is like being handed the key to the camp. However, if we are to supply x to the guard's y, the problem gets considerably trickier, especially if the function is a higher-order polynomial. Only a mathematics club looking for admissions to none but the most accomplished mathematicians may wish to employ such codes! What is more, there could be numerous correct responses, depending on whether the coding function is a polynomial of the second, third, fourth, fifth or higher order, because such polynomials may have more than one root. Typically, higher-order polynomials might be extremely difficult or even impossible to solve. For polynomials beyond the fourth order, the aspirants to the club may need high-speed super-computers to gain entry. In short, while such clubs may prevent the entry of impostors altogether, they may also make it extremely difficult even for their legitimate members to get in.

Another coding scheme could be a series of numbers. For example, a highly exclusive club may use the series of prime numbers as the basis of their code. The guard's clue may be an integer, like 1, 2, 3, 4, etc., while the response expected may be the first, second or third successive prime number, accompanied by a constant factor to be added, subtracted or multiplied.

Imagine a youngster trying to enter the exclusive club of IIMs, trying to get past the Common Admission Test. Many of the questions in such tests revolve around the respondent correctly guessing the next number in a series. For example, you may have a question asking you to figure out the first number (x) in the series such as: x, 9, 11, 15, 17, 21, 23, 27. One may be tempted to respond with 5 because, starting from 9, the periodic difference from the next number works out to 2, 4, 2, 4, 2 and 4, respectively. A ready solution that suggests itself for x is 5. 5 falls in the pattern of the first difference being 4, to yield the pattern 4, 2, 4, 2 ... But this may be a pseudo solution, designed to make a simpleton fall for the obvious, like Duryodhana in the house of Maya or our fiddling around with the pseudo keyhole.

The correct solution could well be 7, if the key is the sequence of prime numbers + 4. If 1 is accepted as the first prime number, then 1+ 4 is 5; the second prime number is 2, and 2 + 4 is 6; the third prime number is 3, and 3 + 4 is 7; the fourth prime number is 5, and 5 + 4 is 9; followed by 7 + 4, 11 + 4, 13 + 4, 17 + 4, 19 + 4, 23 + 4, and so on, as shown in the table.

Serial Integers	1	2	3	4	5	6	7	8	9	10	11	12	...
Prime Number	1	2	3	5	7	11	13	17	19	23	29	31	...
Prime Number + 4	5	6	7 = x	9	11	15	17	21	23	27	33	35	...

And that's exactly what a genre of red-herring locks specializes in. Such locks show a pseudo keyhole here, a misleading rivet there, or a false twist of the key somewhere else – each lock varying minutely from another which you thought was rather similar – and thus defeat you every time. The lock in Figure 21a has many variations. Even the lock shown in Figure 20a is one such and there are literally hundreds of others, in which you may be given a key, but the lock may reveal no keyhole at all – not even a deceptive one! Yes, it is easy to laugh at a bumbling Duryodhana when you know the right answers, keyholes or codes.

Maya's palace, our padlocks and the club using the number codes are all using the principle of 'revealing to conceal'. Even with numbers, the variations to 'show and hide' can be many. For example, let us say, chastened by the above experience, Duryodhana tries his luck another time at yet another gate and this time waits for more observations of interaction between the guard and the members. Let us say, as the first member of the evening arrives, the guard says '1' and gets the reply '1', which turns out to be the right answer; the next member is greeted with the number '2', to which the right response turns out to be '2'; to the third member, the guard says '3' and the member responds with '3' and is let in. Whatever Duryodhana's weaknesses, being dumb isn't one of them. Besides, he has only just been rebuffed in the previous attempt. He is certain that the fourth member will be greeted with a '4'and the response can hardly be expected to be the same number. So he decides to wait, watch and gather more information on the pattern by watching the next member. As the fourth member of the evening comes in, sure enough, the guard says '4', the member responds with '5', and is let in! Aha! Now Duryodhana has it all figured out! Good thing he waited patiently for another member to come by. Clearly, the response of the first, second, third and fourth members were the first, second, third and fourth prime numbers (treating unity as a prime number). So he confidently steps forth, and as he is greeted with '5' by the guard, he confidently responds with '7' – the fifth prime number. Alas, once again he is turned away for the impostor that he is! It turns out that this time, the correct response would be '8'.To 6 it would be 13; to 7, 21; to 8, 34; to 9, 55; to 10, 89; and so forth. Do you get the key?

The Fibonacci Code

Well the guard is using Fibonacci numbers, ignoring the first two Fibonacci numbers, namely 0 and 1. By definition, Fibonacci numbers begin with 0 and 1, and thereafter, each succeeding number is the sum of the previous two Fibonacci numbers.[1] The table indicates the numbers Duryodhana ought to have used in order to sneak into the Pandavas' camp successfully:

Guard	–	–	1	2	3	4	5	6	7	8	9	10	...
Fibonacci Number	0	1	1	2	3	5	8	13	21	34	55	89	...

All right, so the club's security code was based on the Fibonacci numbers. But what's so special about them? Let us look at some well known but interesting aspects of these. Fibonacci numbers, apart from their mathematical property, seem to crop up all over nature. For instance, the number of petals in flowers often follow Fibonacci numbers. For example, the white calla lily has one petal; euphorbia has two; iris, lily and trillium have three; buttercup, columbine, larkspur pinks and wild rose have five; bloodroot and delphiniums, eight; black-eyed Susan, corn marigold, cineraria, ragwort and some varieties of daisies have thirteen; some aster, chicory and Shasta daisy, twenty-one; field daisies, plantain, and pyrethrum, thirty-four (on average); Michaelmas daisies and the stereaceae family have fifty-five and eighty-nine petals. Perhaps you could spend your next summer vacation checking out the veracity of this statement!

Fibonacci numbers also crop up in biological settings. To understand how, consider this particular type of rabbit. Let us say we have a pair that mates at the end of each year, with a gestation period of one year, and that the pair breeds only once a year and produces exactly one pair of baby rabbits – one male and one female – with each pregnancy. Given this condition, how will the population of the rabbits grow in successive years?

We begin the year with one pair. At the end of the first year, the pair mates, but we still have only one pair. At the end of the second year, we have an additional pair, which makes it a total of two pairs. At this point, the first pair mates again, so that at the end of the third year, we have one more pair from the mating of the first, while the second pair is just mating. So at this point, we have three pairs in all. Following the logic closely, we find that at the end of the fourth year, we have five pairs; at the end of seventh year, thirteen pairs, and so on! A similar pattern crops up in the branching of trees, arrangement of leaves on a stem, arrangement of a pine cone, uncurling fern, fruitlets of a pineapple, and so on! The following figure depicts the growth in our rabbit population or the branching off of a tree.

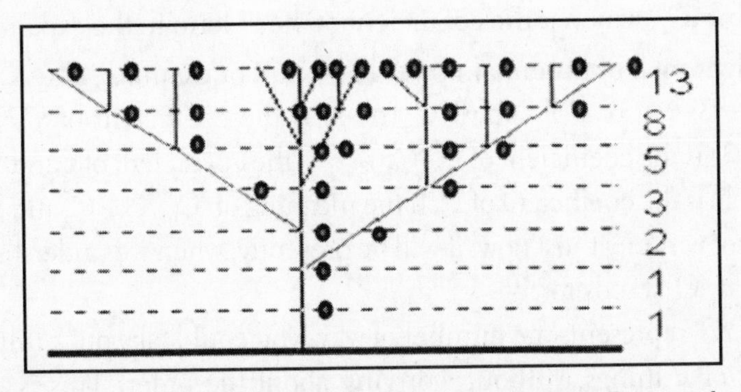

Figure 22 A representation of the growth in the rabbit population or the branching off of a tree

Leonardo Fibonacci of Pisa (1170–1250 AD), better known as Fibonacci, was the number theorist who brought the Aramaic number system we use today, to Europe. He discovered this pattern and observed the similarities with breeding pairs of rabbits and other animals.

Fibonacci numbers also crop up in the toss of coins, or in binomial coefficients. If you are a little lost on what we are talking about, let us take a small detour, and try and understand binomial coefficients.

Binomials

We referred to binomial coefficients in the previous chapter. Let us be clear on what binomials are. Algebraically, a binomial is a polynomial with two terms – the sum of two monomials – often bound by parenthesis when operated upon, like $(a + b)^3$. So then, what are binomial coefficients? These are a family of positive integers which occur as coefficients in the binomial expansion. A binomial coefficient indexed by *n* and *k* is usually written as $\binom{n}{k}$ or ^nC_k, which is the coefficient of the x^k term in the expanded polynomial of binomial power $(1 + x)^n$. For example, $(1 + x)^3 = x^3 + 3x^2 + 3x + 1$. Now, $^3C_0$ (or 1) is the coefficient of x^3; $^3C_1$ (or 3) is the coefficient of x^2, $^3C_2$(or 3)is the coefficient of *x* and $^3C_3$ (or 1) is the coefficient of x^0. If the meaning of $^3C_0$, $^3C_1$, $^3C_2$ and $^3C_3$ is not very clear just now, it will be presently, when we understand what ^nC_k stands for.

^nC_k represents the number of ways you could take out *k* things out of *n* things, without worrying about the order. This is the number of combination of *n* different things taken *k* at a time. If you *did* worry about the order, it would be permutation and not combination. For example, imagine a cocktail of rum, tequila, and blue curacao. It remains the same if you mixed tequila, rum and blue curacao or blue curacao, rum and tequila. In short, the order is unimportant, and the question of how many different kinds of cocktails you can make from a given number of different spirits belongs to the category of combinatorial problems. But imagine the code of your combination lock, which is 473. Clearly, it is different from 374 and 734. Order matters here. This category of problems leads to permutation. In other words, a permutation is an ordered combination or a combination is an unordered permutation.

Now take an ordinary digital lock on a safe with a four-digit code. Let us assume for the sake of simplicity that the four digits are all distinct, that is, no number is repeated. Given that we have in all ten available digits from 0 to 9, how many different four-digit codes are possible? This is a permutation problem, as order of the numbers matters. Thus, the first digit of the code could be any one of the ten single-digit numbers, including 0. Now we have nine digits left. Any one of these could occupy the second digit of the code. Thus, in all, we have ninety permutations so far, that is 10×9. Now we have eight single-digit integers contending for the third place of the code. This makes for $10\times 9\times 8$ permutations, or 720 permutations in all. For the fourth place in the code, we have seven single-digit integers. This gives rise to a total permutation of $10\times 9\times 8\times 7$ or 5,040.This is also expressed as $10!/(10-4)!$[2] On the other hand, if the numbers could be repeated, the permutation works out to $10 \times 10 \times 10 \times 10$ or 10^4 or 10,000. That is, any number from 0000 to 9,999.

But consider an alternative problem involving Draupadi. We know that according to the epic, the Pandavas had a memorandum of understanding to spend one year at a time with Draupadi without intrusions. Supposing we reckon with the first three years in the cycle, in how many different ways can we name the three brothers who would have shared one year each with Draupadi? If we were to list out the names, we would have:

1. Yudhisthira, Bhima, Arjuna
2. Yudhisthira, Bhima, Nakula
3. Yudhisthira, Bhima, Sahadeva
4. Yudhisthira, Arjuna, Nakula
5. Yudhisthira, Arjuna, Sahadeva
6. Yudhisthira, Nakula, Sahadeva
7. Bhima, Arjuna, Nakula
8. Bhima, Arjuna, Sahadeva

9. Bhima, Nakula, Sahadeva
10. Arjuna, Nakula, Sahadeva

Clearly, if the order of the three husbands does not matter, the number of combinations of the husbands Draupadi can have, taking any three in the first three years, is ten. This is also represented by $^5C_3$, which is nothing but $\frac{5!}{3! \times (5-3)!}$ O or 10.[3] This was a simple problem and Draupadi, at a crunch, could have arrived at the answer by exhaustive enumeration of the possibilities, as we did above.

What if our time of reference is the first two years of the cycle? Draupadi could choose to cohabit for a year each with any two (k) of her five husbands (n) over the two year period. She could do this in ^nC_k, $^5C_2$ different ways, which also works out to 10, namely:

1. Yudhisthira, Bhima
2. Yudhisthira, Arjuna
3. Yudhisthira, Nakula
4. Yudhisthira, Sahadeva
5. Bhima, Arjuna
6. Bhima, Nakula
1. Bhima, Sahadeva
8. Arjuna, Nakula,
9. Arjuna, Sahadeva
10. Nakula, Sahadeva

A simpler way to answer the above would have been $^5C_2$ or $\frac{5!}{(5-2)! \times 2!} = 10$, again.

But what if King Dhritarashtra wanted his hundred sons sent to a particularly nefarious and dangerous mission, like playing a practical joke upon Bhima, but at the last moment, wanted to save any two of his favourite sons from harm? In how many different combinations of the sons could the king do so? Surely exhaustive enumeration of the possibilities is bound to prove too exhausting! The simple answer will be $^{100}C_{98} = \frac{100}{98! \times 2!} = 4{,}950$.

Now, let us recall the coefficients of a binomial expansion from the previous chapter, $(x + y)^n$, where x + y is any binomial and n is a whole number.

$$(x + y)^0 = 1$$
$$(x + y)^1 = x + y$$
$$(x + y)^2 = x^2 + 2xy + y^2$$
$$(x + y)^3 = x^3 + 3x^2y + 3xy^2 + y^3$$
$$(x + y)^4 = x^4 + 4x^3y + 6x^2y^2 + 4xy^3 + y^4$$
$$(x + y)^5 = x^5 + 5x^4y + 10x^3y^2 + 10x^2y^3 + 5xy^4 + y^5$$
$$(x + y)^6 = x^6 + 6x^5y + 15x^4y^2 + 20x^3y^3 + 15x^2y^4 + 6xy^5 + y^6$$
$$\ldots$$

Notice that the answer to the problem of combination of three or two husbands that Draupadi could cohabit with in a given year is nothing but the coefficients pertaining to x^3 or x^2, in the expansion of, say $(x + y)^5$, which is 10.

Arranging the binomial coefficients ^nC_k into rows for successive values of *n*, in which *k* is zero or any positive integer from 1 to n, gives a triangular arrangement called Pascal's triangle, which goes as follows:

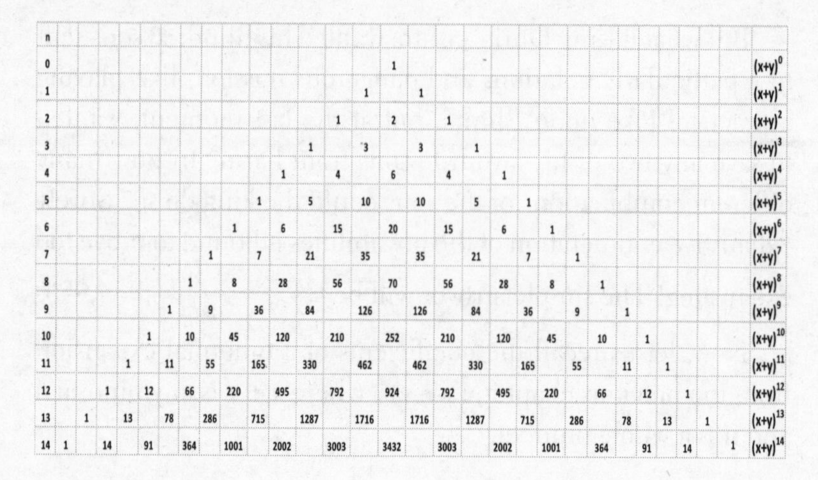

n																														
0															1															$(x+y)^0$
1														1		1														$(x+y)^1$
2													1		2		1													$(x+y)^2$
3												1		3		3		1												$(x+y)^3$
4											1		4		6		4		1											$(x+y)^4$
5										1		5		10		10		5		1										$(x+y)^5$
6									1		6		15		20		15		6		1									$(x+y)^6$
7								1		7		21		35		35		21		7		1								$(x+y)^7$
8							1		8		28		56		70		56		28		8		1							$(x+y)^8$
9						1		9		36		84		126		126		84		36		9		1						$(x+y)^9$
10					1		10		45		120		210		252		210		120		45		10		1					$(x+y)^{10}$
11				1		11		55		165		330		462		462		330		165		55		11		1				$(x+y)^{11}$
12			1		12		66		220		495		792		924		792		495		220		66		12		1			$(x+y)^{12}$
13		1		13		78		286		715		1287		1716		1716		1287		715		286		78		13		1		$(x+y)^{13}$
14	1		14		91		364		1001		2002		3003		3432		3003		2002		1001		364		91		14		1	$(x+y)^{14}$

And so on.

How is this triangle built? At the apex is the number 1. In each row thereafter, the first and the last numbers are always 1. In any given row, the second number is the sum of the first and second number of the row just above; the third number is the sum of the second and third number of the row right above, etc. For example, take the sixth row, or the row corresponding to n = 6. The first number is 1; the second number is 6, the sum of 1 and 5 in the row above; the third number is 15, the sum of 5 and 10 in the row above; the fourth number is 20, the sum of 10 and 10; and so on. But what use is this triangle?

In Pascal's triangle, the problem of combination of three or two husbands that Draupadi could live with in a year provided is given by the third and fourth coefficient against row 5 above ($^5C_3$ and $^5C_2$, which work out to 10 and 10, respectively).

It can be seen that the number in each array is nothing but the coefficient of the terms of the expansions shown earlier. Thus, any number in a given row is denoted by the simple formula ^nC_k, where *n* corresponds to the row and *k* to the position of the coefficient, whether 0th, first, second or third and so on, in a given row.

Now for instance, the coefficients for the expansion of $(x + y)^{10}$, or the coefficients corresponding to the terms with x^{10}, x^9, x^8 etc., are obtained from the row n = 10 in Pascal's triangle. For example:

the 0th coefficient is ${}^{10}C_0$ (= 1), pertaining to x^{10},
the first coefficient is ${}^{10}C_1$ (= 10), pertaining to x^9y,
the second coefficient is ${}^{10}C_2$ (= 45), pertaining to x^8y^2,
the third coefficient is ${}^{10}C_3$ (= 120), pertaining to x^7y^3,
the fourth coefficient is ${}^{10}C_4$ (= 210), pertaining to x^6y^4, and
the fifth coefficient is ${}^{10}C_5$ (= 252), pertaining to x^5y^5...

Suppose we want to know the probability of landing heads and tails if an unbiased coin is tossed five times. We then refer to the array against n = 5, whose successive coefficients are 1, 5, 10, 10, 5, and 1. The coefficients add up to 32. Thus the probability that we shall land five heads and no tails (or five tails and no heads) is 1/32; the probability that there will be four heads and one tail or four tails and one head will be 5/32; the probability of there being three heads and two tails or three tails and two heads will be 10/32. Now surely you are ready to toss 7, 8 or 20 coins in the air and compute the probabilities of landing four heads or six tails, and so forth, right?

Back to Fibonacci Numbers

Going back to Fibonacci numbers, how do binomial coefficients lead to Fibonacci numbers? Let us take a look at Figure 23, which is nothing but the Pascal's triangle in a left justified format. Now add the numbers in each successive diagonal in the triangle below from the north-eastern to the south-westerly direction and you will find the Fibonacci numbers!

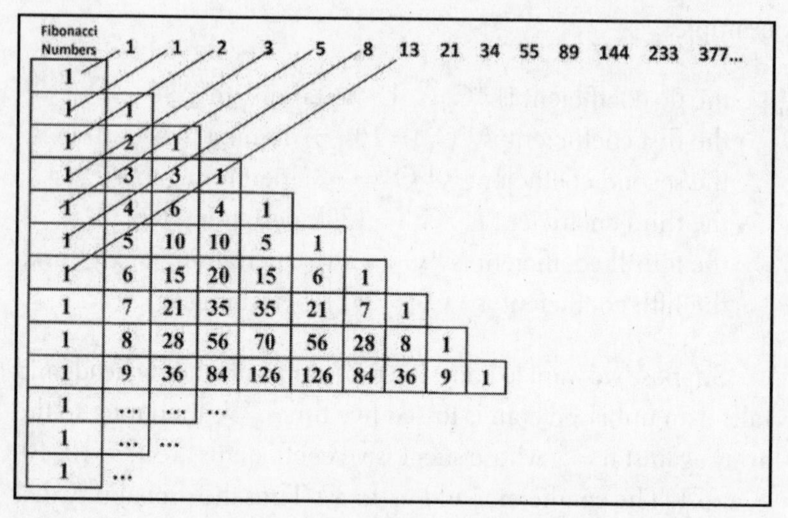

Figure 23 A representation of the relationship between binomial coefficients, Pascal's triangle and Fibonacci numbers

Fibonacci numbers find applications in such seemingly unrelated areas as Euclid's algorithm to determine the greatest common divisor of two integers, Zeckendorf's theorem (that every positive integer can be uniquely written as the sum of one or more Fibonacci numbers such that the sum does not feature any two consecutive Fibonacci numbers), the golden ratio, and in the conversion of miles to kilometres in a host of other unrelated areas!

Consider this. Golden ratio (usually denoted by the Greek alphabet ϕ) is an irrational number that is equal to its own reciprocal plus one, so that its square is nothing but the number itself plus 1. In other words, the golden ratio $\phi = 1/\phi + 1$; or $\phi^2 = \phi + 1$; or $\phi^2 - \phi - 1 = 0$.This is a simple quadratic equation in ϕ, so that $\phi = (1 \pm \sqrt{5})/2$.[4]

This gives us either 1.618033989 or –0.618033989. The first of these numbers is the golden ratio, while the second, which is the negative of its reciprocal, has its own applications.

What is interesting is that if you compute the ratio of the successive Fibonacci numbers, say 1/1, 2/1, 3/2, 5/3, 8/5, 13/8, 21/13, etc., they gradually approach a limit and the limit is called the golden number!

And this number corresponds very closely with the conversion factor between a mile and a kilometre, which is 1.609344, though this may well be purely accidental.

The fact is, we could choose virtually any kind of series as a code. And that's exactly what happens with many of the locks in this genre as well. Little alterations in each lock serve to trick you every time.

Doing a Draupadi at a bumbling Duryodhana is possible only when you know the right answers, hidden steps to keyholes, or codes!

FOUR

YUDHISTHIRA'S GAMBLE, CHANCY LOCKS AND MATHEMATICAL PROBABILITIES

A Dripping and Angry Duryodhana and an Attempt to Disrupt the Rajasuya

Derisive laughter is never balm to frayed nerves, and if Duryodhana emerged mad as a wet hen from the pool, it ought to be understandable, especially given his surly disposition. And as the Pandavas would have you believe, Duryodhana never did much good, mad or otherwise.

Had you been an onlooker, you would have seen Duryodhana collect himself out of the pool, his dignity dripping, his head in turmoil, trying to devise a way to get even. He simply had to show that woman that it never paid to laugh at Duryodhana. He would show her husbands that it didn't pay to mess with Duryodhana.

Thus insulted, incensed Duryodhana's mind continued to work overtime, scheming how he could possibly disrupt the proceedings of the rajasuya, when opportunity came his way as the Pandavas chose Lord Krishna, the Yadava chief of Dwarka, over all others, to accord the highest honour at the yajna. Duryodhana was much closer to Krishna's elder brother Balarama – his mace guru – than to the wily younger brother himself, about whom his sentiments were, at best, mixed. And when he heard his good friend Shishupala – the powerful king of Chedi – muttering his displeasure at Yudhisthira's choice of Krishna for the highest honour, Duryodhana seized the opportunity and stoked Shishupala's spark of annoyance into a roaring flame of ranting and raving anger, culminating in his challenging the choice openly.

The Slaying of Shishupala

Shishupala, encouraged by powerful Duryodhana, raised his objection at Yudhisthira selecting for the honour a milkman of doubtful parentage, with no royal lineage, and the devious hand behind the slaying of the valiant Jarasandha. He pointed out the unsuitability of the choice, especially when there were gurus of the stature of Drona, Parashurama and Kripacharya, or if one preferred mighty kings of known valour, Duryodhana or Mrityunjaya, or he himself – the mighty king of Chedi, in all humility – present in the assembly as legitimate claimants to the high honour. This, he thundered, was indeed a deliberate slur to the dignity of the Kauravas, their gurus, their families and their friends. He bellowed that Krishna was a mere playboy cowherd, and a born thief, starting as a regular little butter-thief who also stole feathers from the tails of peacocks in his spare time, graduating to stealing the skirts of bathing maidens, and who knows what else. Why, he was not even fit to sit among the kings present at the rajasuya, leave alone be accorded the highest honour. Matters rapidly deteriorated from this point onwards, just stopping short of the kind of ruckus usually witnessed in unruly Assemblies or on prime-time television debates. Shishupala went ahead and challenged Krishna to a duel, and raised enough rabble in the assembly for Krishna to figure that the only way to stop the loudmouth was to accept his dare.

To cut a long story short, events culminated in Lord Krishna letting his spinning disk fly off his index finger at Shishupala's throat. The sharp, serrated edge of the disc cut through Shishupala's neck and the matter was settled, leaving Duryodhana surlier than ever.

The Gambling Plot That Banked on a Weakness

Cut to the quick by the triple affront to his sensibilities – namely, having to accept the superiority of the Pandavas implicit in the rajasuya yajna, Draupadi's snicker, and his friend Shishupala's decapitation – the rajasuya was hardly an agreeable event for Duryodhana. The months that followed were near torture. Even the little sleep he managed to steal off his insomnia disappeared. He only had to shut his eyes for the insults suffered at the rajasuya to dance before his eyes like performing monkeys. He had always been a hard worker when it came to plotting against the Pandavas, and he used the extra waking hours to work harder yet.

At this stage, it must be said that Yudhisthira's keen interest in gambling was public knowledge. Also, it was not honourable for a king to spurn an invitation from another king for a game of dice. Armed with these two bits of knowledge, and after some crafty consultation with his nimble-fingered uncle, Shakuni – a known dice-sharper – Duryodhana devised an elaborate gambling tournament of regal stakes. The idea was that Shakuni, with his sleight of hand, would ensure that the 'game of chance' against the straight-laced Yudhisthira was nothing of the sort, and that the all-or-nothing game would ensure the ruin of the Pandavas. All that was needed was to send Yudhisthira an invite that he couldn't refuse.

Much thought went into choosing the courier to extend the

invitation, and the task, for various reasons, fell upon Vidhura – a grand uncle of sorts to both the Kauravas and Pandavas, born to sage Vyasa and the maid of the queen-grandmothers, Ambika and Ambalika. Vidhura was a respected elder in the courts of Hastinapura, and was held in high esteem by the Pandavas. Shrewd Duryodhana knew there was no way Yudhisthira would decline an invite carried personally by Vidhura.

Yudhisthira, as mentioned earlier, had a weak spot for gambling, and he accepted the invitation against the advice of his counsellors, including his brothers, who sensed that the game would be rigged. That a king could not honourably decline such an invitation was his winning argument and Yudhisthira landed up at Hastinapura with his brothers and their joint-wife in tow on the due date. Duryodhana had gone to some pains to match the majesty of the event they had witnessed in Indraprastha and so the setting was fit for the kings.

The Kaurava versus Pandava roll of dice commenced. The atmosphere was as charged as an India-Pak cricket match. The chosen game was that of chausar – a board shaped like the 'plus' sign. As the two cousins sat facing each other, Yudhisthira chose to throw his own dice, while Duryodhana appointed Shakuni to do the honours on his behalf.

At first, the fortunes seemed to swing either way, as may be expected in a pure game of chance. However, as the tournament gathered momentum, Yudhisthira made some initial headway, making some quick wins as the dice fell his way, while Shakuni simply couldn't seem to get his throws right. Yudhisthira seemed to get on to a winning streak as Duryodhana seemed to lose much of his collection of jewels, gold, rubies, pearls, diamonds, and other assorted precious stones and metals from his treasury. Yudhisthira kept throwing self-satisfied glances at his brothers, reminding them how their reservations were misplaced and how this entertaining game was adding to their treasury impressively. His shoulders were thrown back, he laughed more, and his jokes and conversation became louder. Soon, he upped the stakes further, confident that his winnings weren't so much luck as his brilliant skill at throwing dice – not unlike investors who come to regard themselves financial geniuses in a random bull market. And through all this, Duryodhana kept glaring at Shakuni darkly, wondering if he had not overestimated his uncle's dice-throwing skills.

The Loss of Kingdom, Wife and Honour

Either Shakuni had had enough of fair play, or more likely, he had deliberately been throwing the dice so as to let Yudhisthira win for a while, in order to nudge him towards higher stakes. Before long, the course of the game swung the Kauravas' way. As the game progressed, it became increasingly evident that Shakuni was somehow able to bid the dice to fall as he pleased again and again, while Yudhisthira could only watch helplessly. Try as he might, he was able to find nothing wrong with Shakuni's throw, though one could see from the result of the throw that what ought to have been a fair game of probabilities was anything but that. Before long, Yudhisthira lost his earlier winnings, his own treasury, and then his kingdom, his brothers, himself, and eventually even his wife, to Duryodhana, as he continued betting recklessly.

And thus did Yudhisthira gamble away his kingdom, his family, and all shreds of honour, leading to a thirteen-year exile in the wilderness, which was the precondition for having any chance at regaining their lost kingdom.

Chancy Locks

The game of chance reminds me to ask you if you have ever seen a chancy lock – a lock, the opening of which is probabilistic? If the question foxes you, check out the lock in Figure 24. There are two different keyholes on the lock and there are two different keys. One of them opens the lock and the other locks it. The key shown on the left, which opens the lock, works on the keyhole on the left and the key that closes it works on the other keyhole.

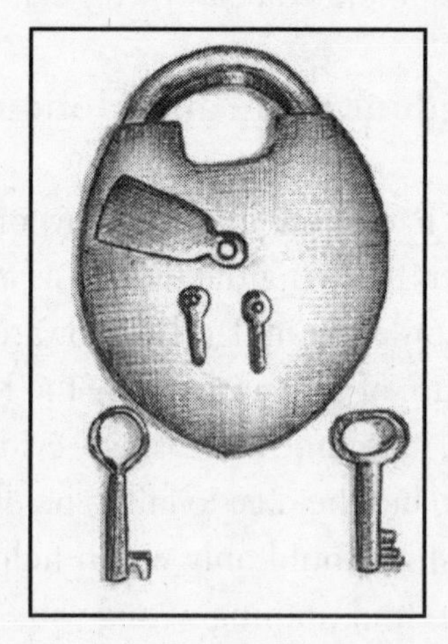

Figure 24 A very rare, old lock from Rajasthan/Gujarat/Aligarh, with two keys and two keyholes; one key closes the lock and the other opens it (13 × 10.5 × 2 cms)

Now, someone attempting to pick this lock may well toil away to fit a key in the wrong keyhole, which ends up being the key that cannot open the lock but is the closing key! The probability of picking the lock is thus nearly halved. That's why this lock – a variant of which we will see in Chapter 7 as well – qualifies to be called a probabilistic lock.

Mathematical Probabilities

In the mathematical world, the theory of probability deals with the analysis of random events or processes which by definition are not deterministic. Why would, for example, the toss of a coin or the roll of a die be called a random event? If the toss is a random event, each toss is independent of the previous or subsequent tosses. When it is repeated a large number of times, the sequence of tosses begins to reveal a certain pattern, which can help predict the outcome of a toss.

Let us look into the simple matter of probabilities surrounding the throw of two six-sided dice.

A little reflection reveals that two six-sided dice can fall in thirty-six different ways (each of the six numbers in one of the dice being associated with six other numbers in the other, or 6 × 6 ways). Now, the total of the numbers we get when the two dice are thrown together can range from 2 to 12. What is the probability that the next throw of the two dice would yield a total of 2, or 3, or 4, or any other number up to 12? The total number of ways one can get a total of 2 is just one, namely, a throw of 1 and 1. Similarly, the total number of ways one can get a total of 3 is two – a throw of 1 and 2 or 2 and 1; the ways one can get a total of 4 is three – 1 and 3, 2 and 2, and 3 and 1. But since the total number of possible throws is thirty-six, the probability of getting a total of 2 must be 1/36 (or 2.78%), a total of 3 must be 2/36 (5.56%), a total of 4 must be 3/36 (8.33%), and so on. The table here shows the details of all the probabilities.

Total of the Dice Roll	Number of Possible Ways/ Total Number of Ways	Probability
2	1/36	2.78%
3	2/36	5.56%
4	3/36	8.33%
5	4/36	11.11%
6	5/36	13.89%
7	6/36	16.67%
8	5/36	13.89%
9	4/36	11.11%
10	3/36	8.33%
11	2/36	5.56%
12	1/36	2.78%

Figure 25 A table representing the probability of the total points one is likely to get when one rolls two dice

As you can see, 7 is the most common roll with two six-sided dice. It can happen in six different ways: 1and 6, 2 and 5, 3 and 4, 4 and 3, 5 and 2, and 6 and 1. It's six times more likely that you'll roll a 7 than a 2 or a 12. It is thrice as likely as throwing a total of 3 or 11. And twice as likely that you'll roll a 7 than a 4 or a 10. However, it's only 1.2 times more likely that you'll roll a 7 than a 6 or an 8.

Another way of looking at these numbers is that if you keep throwing the two dice repeatedly, you may expect to see six 7s for every 2 or 12 rolled; or a 4 or 10 for every two 7s rolled, and so on. And yet, neither the opening of the lock nor the roll of dice would follow this precise prediction! In other words, bet on the prediction by all means, but cautiously.

Let us conjecture on how Shakuni probably cheated Yudhisthira. In all likelihood, he was throwing a pair of loaded dice, that is dice in which each side does not have an equal probability of occurrence. This can happen, for instance, if you hollow out a die lopsidedly and fill it with, say, a tiny bit of lead, and then close it neatly. You may now have a die in which, for instance, the chance of throwing a 6 may not be 1/6, but much higher, if the lead were loaded in the direction of 6. If Shakuni were aware of this but not Yudhisthira, it is quite possible that Yudhisthira bet on the assumption of an even die, while Shakuni did so with the knowledge that the probability of the occurrence of a 6 was more than one-in-six.

Take a look at the lock in figures 26a and 26b.

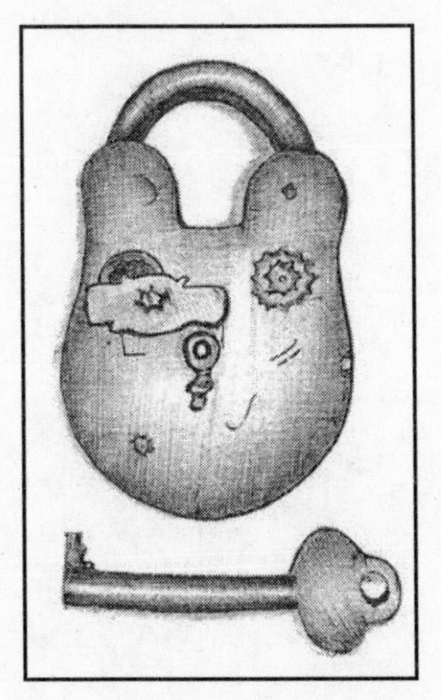

Figure 26a The side from which the key opens the lock (8 × 5 × 1.5 cms)

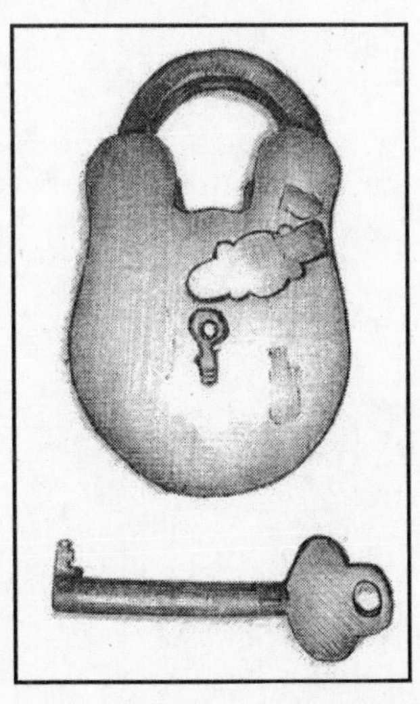

Figure 26b Other side from which the key closes the lock

The lock looks rather ordinary, with a single key, if you do not know any better, like Yudhisthira. On the other hand, if you have more information, like Shakuni, you will know that this contraption has different orifices for opening and closing. In short, it has a keyhole on either side! Inserting the key on one side opens the lock, while the same key, when turned on the other side, closes the lock. Now if you do not know which side the key should be inserted to open it, the probability of the lock being picked reduces to nearly half in a given time frame, because even if a lock-picker manages to fit a key into the keyhole, the probability that it is the right keyhole is one-half.

If you thought that your skills in gambling and picking locks could keep you safe from hunger and privation, think again, for fickle probabilities, devious cousins and chancy locks may have other things in store for you!

FIVE

HANUMAN'S TAIL, THE MONKEY LOCK AND LONG-TAILED DISTRIBUTIONS

One Day in the Second Innings of Wilderness

Having lost their kingdom and their honour to the Kauravas in the game of dice, the Pandavas were forced into a thirteen-year exile. The burden and disgrace of the severe atrocity, followed by the insult their wife Draupadi had been subjected to in the assembly hall of the Kauravas, sat heavily upon the conscience of the Pandava brothers as they roamed the forests preparing to recover their lost kingdom some day. Before long, it was evident that in spite of the promises of the Kauravas, mere completion of their tenure in the forest would not allow them to regain their kingdom, and that the Kauravas – a mighty force to reckon with – would not yield an inch of their kingdom without a bloody fight. Folks who are down and out, and have lost their shirts and wife to gambling, do not always have too many powerful friends, while rulers, irrespective of the degree of their villainy, almost always command friends galore. And this worry nagged the Pandavas as well as the distraught Draupadi.

The Pandavas had sought refuge in the Dwaitavana. The thick forest, with its beautiful lake, was home to many sages performing severe penances – with some standing on a single toe of one leg, others on their heads, and so forth – even as they braved the elements out in the open and ants built their mud-hills all over them. Worse, these sages were constantly harassed by the evil denizens of the forest whose favourite pastime seemed to be to badger emaciated Brahmins. The friendless Pandavas had befriended these Brahmins and taken them under their protection. And the sages were most grateful for the presence of the Kshatriya warriors in their midst.

Vyasa was one of these sages. During one of his visits to the Pandavas, he advised Yudhisthira to think a little strategically ahead, knowing that a war with the Kauravas was inevitable. He granted that Yudhisthira had valiant Arjuna and mighty Bhima to count upon, but would they suffice against the mighty army of the Kauravas, which comprised warriors like Drona, Bhishma, Karna, Kripa, Duryodhana, Dushasana and Ashwatthama, he asked. It was clear that desperate times were ahead and some desperate measures were called for.

Arjuna Sets off for the Himalayas

Vyasa argued that since Arjuna had an influential pater, Lord Indra, should they not dispatch him to the Himalayas to do some serious penance, gain his father's blessings, and obtain some high-potency weaponry on the side? And while at it, he may as well win the favour of other gods, such as Rudra, Varuna, Yama and Kubera, and pick up what he could. The good guru also taught Yudhisthira some secret mantras – which could summon the very gods – and advised him to impart the same to Arjuna in turn. And with a final word of caution not to stay put at the same spot for too long, the sage took leave.

Yudhisthira in turn imparted to Arjuna the words of wisdom Vyasa had given him and conveyed the mantras Vyasa had entrusted him with, just in case he needed some divine help during his arduous trek. So Arjuna packed his backpack – which was actually a quiver – and set out for the Himalayas to seek out Indra and obtain from him some divine instruments of warfare.

Arjuna's departure might have paved the way for greater per-capita time for the remaining Pandavas with Draupadi, but the brothers and Draupadi alike certainly missed Arjuna. To Draupadi for sure, the sunshine seemed a dash less bright; the twitter of birds a notch less melodious; the breeze a trifle stale; the twinkle of the stars a watt dimmer, and their sprinkle on the night sky a touch thinner; and the four brothers seemed one brother too few.

Draupadi on Bhima's Shoulder

To humour a depressed Draupadi, they tried a change of scene by moving to a different forest, even if it implied more legwork.

It was not unusual for dainty Draupadi, reduced below size zero with all the walking in the wild, to ride upon the shoulders of one or the other of the swarthy brothers, but mostly upon Bhima's, who was the swarthiest. It is thus perched high up (for Bhima was also a hand taller than most mortals) that the ethereal fragrance of saugandhika – the queen of flowers – wafted into her pert nostrils. A couple of deep sniffs, and she made up her mind that she simply had to have the flower. Would Bhima kindly go get her a bunch, please? Caring men get flowers for their women today. And they did so even then. And Bhima erupted with the joy children display when the teacher asks them to run an errand. And the good, simple man took off in search of the flower. Given its strong fragrance, he didn't find it hard to follow the scent.

The Insolent Monkey

It was one thing to know which way one had to head, but quite another to actually head that way, what with the thick forest anything but yielding, friendly or familiar. Just as Bhima reached the foot of a hill, the scent seemed to lead him to its steep crest. At the same time, his nose began to twitch as it detected another mysterious odour. Soon the mystery cleared, even if it blocked his only path to the top of the hill. The offending obstruction to his nostrils and legs alike was an old, oafish monkey, idly slouching on the ground, with its long tail sweeping right across the narrow trail.

Bhima's peremptory command to get out of his way notwithstanding, the monkey did not budge, and, unimpressed, opened one half of an eye, with just the white showing, and pleaded with just a hint of an insolent smile at the corner of its lips, 'I am too feeble and old to move. Why don't you just go around or simply jump over my tail? Surely that can't be a great deal of effort for a strapping lad like you?' A reasonable request from a reasonable monkey, one would think. It is not for us to wonder why a warrior of Bhima's stature would pitch his ego against a monkey, but Bhima was quick to take offence at the impudent monkey. Some folks might have been taken by surprise by a talking monkey; but just then, Bhima was more struck by the insolence of the monkey than its talking abilities. Red in the face, he roared with anger, 'Don't you know who I am, you wretched simian?' That may have been an original dialogue then, but ever since, has been repeated by millions upon millions of mighty Indians attempting to browbeat anyone they consider their inferior!

When the monkey showed no recognition of who Bhima was,

the mighty warrior decided it was time to introduce himself to the sprawled primate. While he may not exactly have whipped out a visiting card, he introduced himself modestly as Vayuputra, Kuntiputra, the mighty Kshatriya of the Kurus, the mightiest of the Pandavas, slayer of Hidimba, the scourge of raakshasas, the sutasoma – he of the thousand Soma sacrifices, Bhima himself, no less. This was expected to shake the monkey out of its stupor, but it didn't.

The bored monkey sighed and reiterated in a thin voice, the half-eye opening no wider, that it was too feeble to even move its tail. If Bhima didn't want to go around or jump over the tail, there was nothing to it but for Bhima to move it from the path and march on.

A Tail Tackle and a Brother Revealed

This proposition appealed to Bhima's reason. Besides, which one of us, as a kid, has not harboured the secret ambition to hold a monkey by its long, tantalizing tail, if only to hoist it briefly and watch its expression? Perhaps the child in Bhima warmed to this imagery, but he reined in the temptation, and instead, tried to kick the tail haughtily out of his way, only to nearly fracture his toe on something very hard. Darn! He must have been careless! He took better aim this time and delivered a kick that would have made Maradona proud in his heydays. He might as well have kicked a cement truck or its equivalent of the time, for the effort nearly fractured his ankle. What with the anger, pain and the insult, Bhima decided to teach the impudent monkey a memorable lesson. So he bent down and clutched the tail with both his hands and gave it a mighty heave. So powerful was the yank that Bhima's grip slipped off the tail and he landed on his considerable haunches, cutting a less-than-dignified figure.

As the monkey continued to grin sedately at the supine Bhima, realization finally dawned upon the somewhat slow but basically good-natured hulk that this was no ordinary monkey. Truth be told, the monkey business had humbled him. The rest of the story – about the monkey revealing its real identity as none other than Lord Hanuman (Bhima's own elder brother, being also born of the wind god); Bhima learning his lesson in humility; Lord Hanuman giving Bhima half his strength and adding his voice to Bhima's so that every time he gave a war cry, his strength and powerful voice would be added to that of Bhima's; and the devoted husband proceeding to fetch the flower for Draupadi – is not germane to our story here. What is germane is that, in this story, the tail was the key to open a power-drunk Bhima to lessons in humility, which connects to the next set of locks we will discuss.

Monkey Locks

Take a look at figures 27a, 27b and 28. We have two versions of monkeys, which – no prizes for guessing – are also padlocks.

In Figure 27a, the head is attached to the shackle, which is released when the tail (the key) is pushed up the keyhole in the rear (indignity unintended).

In Figure 28, the shackle is attached to the chin, which the key inserted through the bottom pushes up through a hole in the head, while the head itself remains attached to the neck.

In both the locks, the tail is the key. Literally. If you want to open either of these locks, you will have to handle their tails with some respect. (The lock in figures 27a and 27b came without a

Figure 27a Monkey lock in closed position, with the key (tail) inserted (5.5 × 3 × 2 cms)

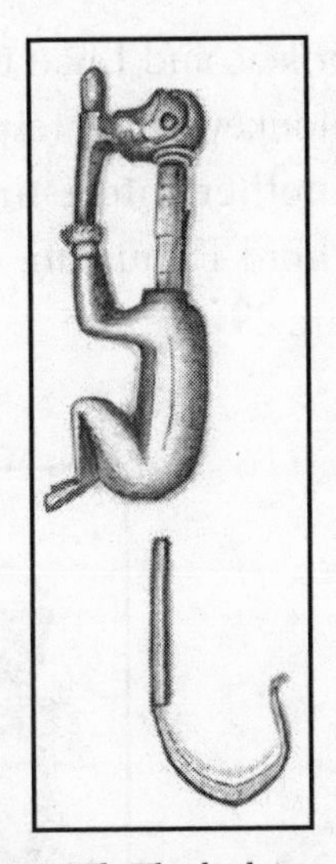

Figure 27b The lock in open position; head attached to the shackle is released

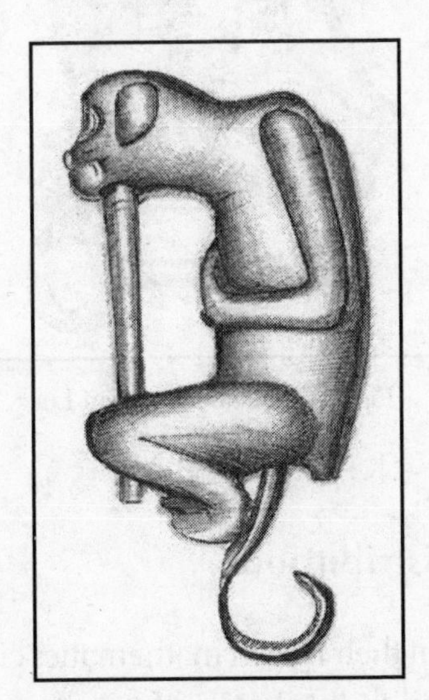

Figure 28 Shackle at the chin; closed position, with the key (tail) inserted (6 × 2.5 × 1.5 cms)

tail or key, and I had to work on the key myself, thus providing the monkey with a respectable tail.)

Another interesting lock is in the form of our monkey god, Lord Hanuman, with the key applied to his belly button (Figure 29).

Figure 29 The Hanuman Lock
(10 × 7 × 2.5 cms)

Thin-tailed Distributions

Tails aren't without their role in mathematics either. In probability theory, the probability distributions typically come with tails. Like any tail, these can be thin, fat, heavy, long or short.

The tails may or may not be exponentially bounded – an exponentially bounded tail being a long and thin tail which forever approaches the x-axis without ever really touching it or, rather, coming down to the value of 0 (see Figure 30: where the two tails of the graph asymptotically approach the base line). The standard normal distribution is an exponentially bounded distribution. In other words, it has a long, thin tail, which means that observations far from the mean are extremely unlikely. The standard normal distribution is a continuous probability distribution, which is typically used as a first approximation to describe real-valued random variables which tend to bunch around a single mean value. A good example of normal distribution in real life may be the height of the adult male population in a city. As can be expected, if the mean height of the population is, say, 5'7", it is highly unlikely that there will be observations with people taller

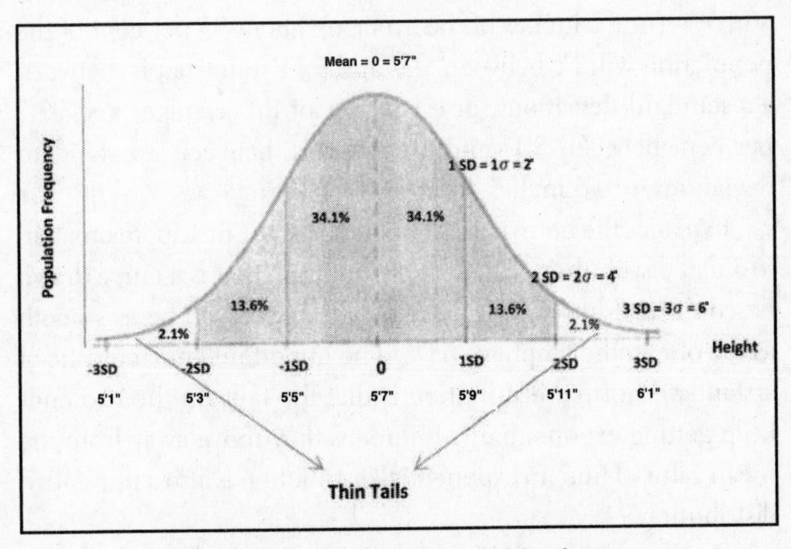

Figure 30 An example of thin-tailed distributions

than 7' or shorter than 4'. Another example could be the age of graduate students.

A great many natural and social phenomena tend to approximate a normal distribution. A theoretical normal distribution has a symmetrical curve, like a bell or a camel's hump as shown in the graph given. For a standard normal distribution, or a normal curve with a perfect bell shape, the mean is zero, while the variance is one.

The graph indicates the height of adult men in a city. The curve tells us that a majority of men will have a height of about 5'7", called the mean height. This mean corresponds to the mean zero. Let us assume that the standard deviation of the height distribution of this population is, say, 2 inches. This corresponds to one standard deviation. Given that the distribution is normally distributed, it also means that nearly 68 per cent of the city's adult male population will have a height somewhere between 5'5" and 5'9" (or ±2 inches of the average); about 95 per cent of the population will be between 5'3" and 5'11" tall (that is, between ±2 standard deviations, or ±4 inches of the average) and 99.7 per cent between 5'1" and 6'1" (that is, between ±3 standard deviations, or ±6 inches of the average).

In reality, the normal distribution is only the first approximation to a real distribution. The real distribution, that is a curve drawn based on real-life observations, is hardly likely to be as smooth as the one in the graph we have. The important characteristic of a standard normal distribution is that the tails on the two ends keep getting exponentially thinner as they move away from the mean value. Thus, an exponential distribution is also a thin-tailed distribution.

On the other hand, in probability theory, there are also heavy tailed probability distributions whose tails are not exponentially bounded and are heavier than those of the exponential distributions. These distributions are also often skewed, or may be flatter or steeper than normal distributions. In some applications, it may be only the right or left tail that may be fat or heavy and of interest to us, while in others, both ends may be fat or heavy. It may be noted that some statisticians do make a nuanced distinction between fat and heavy tailed distributions.

Fat-tailed Distributions

Heavy or fat tails come in two varieties – long or short. But distributions with such tails are technically called long-tailed and sub-exponential distributions. Most fat-tailed distributions we encounter belong to the latter category. The term 'heavy tailed' is also used for any distribution that has a tail heavier than the normal distribution.

A good example of a fat-tailed distribution may be the distribution of city sizes, in that, while most cities are small, a handful are so large as to capture a sizeable population of the total. Fat-tailed distributions are also frequently encountered in the world of finance, where probabilities of rare events do not appear to be all that small as may be predicted by theory. An example may be the Black Monday in October of 1987, when floors across the world stock markets caved in overnight, leaving investors nowhere to run for cover, or the Far Eastern financial crisis in the summer of 1997, or the financial debacle of 2008 worldwide.

Take an example from our everyday lives: namely, the frequency of distribution of words in most texts. Some words occur very often in a given text. For instance, the most frequently occurring word in the English language is 'the', followed by 'of', 'and', 'a', 'to', 'in', 'is', 'you', 'that' and 'it'. Words such as 'out', 'them', 'then', 'she', 'many', 'some', 'so', 'these', 'would' and 'other' – ranking between 50 and 100 in the frequency of occurrence – occur often, but a little less frequently than the first ten. Other words, such as 'avoid', 'daily', 'combine', 'attached', 'frighten' and 'recommend' rank between 1190 and 1200 in the frequency of occurrence, and we see them quite infrequently.[1] And some words occur so rarely that one may pass through a lifetime without ever encountering them – for example, abacinate, batrachophagous, bromidrosis, dactylion, or estrapade, which go towards making a *lo-------ng* tail of words occurring very rarely.

The first twenty-five most frequently occurring words are used in about one-third of everyday writing, while the first hundred words appear in about half of all normal English writing, and the first 1,000 words are used in 89 per cent of everyday writing. If we were to plot various words on the x-axis against the frequency of their occurrence on the y-axis, we may get a truncated fat-tailed distribution like the one shown in Figure 31.

It can be seen that a fat-tailed distribution implies a large number of observations in the 'tail' of the distribution, often far from the mean. Though this characteristic need not apply to all fat-tailed distributions, but it gets the idea across.

Another instance of fat tails is when events with a low probability actually do occur, after which people tend to overestimate the likelihood that they will occur again. So if an earthquake strikes a certain area, the number of people who buy earthquake insurance goes up, even though the likelihood of another one rocking the same area remains unchanged. Here

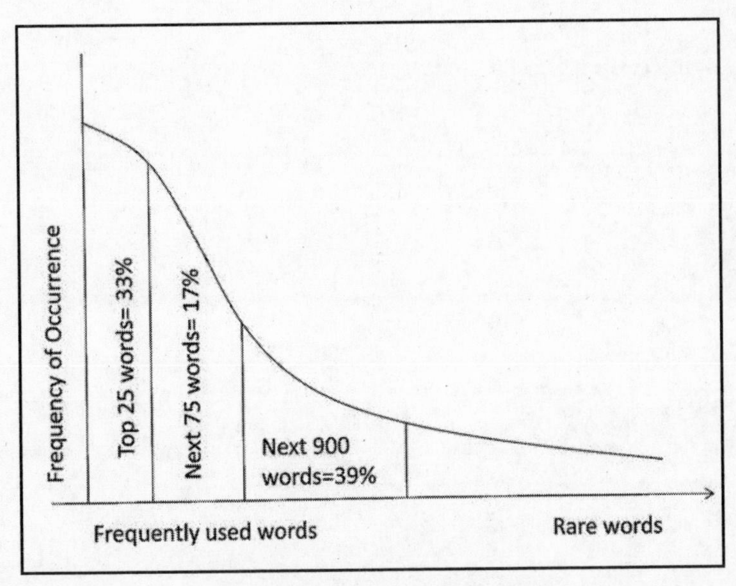

Figure 31 A fat-tailed distribution

again, the normal distribution of what a bell curve would predict is replaced by a fat-tailed distribution. The normal bell curve of prediction is skewed into a fat-tailed distribution model, showing the increased feeling of people that the low-probability event (another earthquake) will happen again.

Ah, so there is more to tails than you had bargained for, right?

SIX

THE ENCHANTED POOL, A LOCK THAT THWARTS INSERTION OF THE KEY AND PROBLEMS THAT RESIST DIRECT ATTACKS

End of the Tunnel

Consequent to their gambling losses, the Pandavas had been dispatched to twelve years of vanvaas (exile into forests), with the thirteenth year to be lived incognito. The idea was that if they succeeded in following all these conditions, they would be entitled to claim their kingdom back. Duryodhana had agreed to this condition with the sage understanding that with thousands of his spies planted all around, there was no way the Pandavas could remain incognito for a whole year. They would be dug out even if they disguised themselves as earthworms.

Arjuna was back from his trip to the Himalayas and the Pandavas were nearing the end of their twelfth year of exile. The thirteenth and the riskiest year of incognito-living lurked just round the corner. The brothers had learnt their lessons well and were averse to taking any more silly risks just as the end of the tunnel was nigh. They were living a quiet life in a humble abode adjacent to a poor Brahmin's hut. One day, a celestial deer came around and was scratching its antlers against the Brahmin's arani (wooden blocks, which when rubbed together, provide sparks for fire) one fine morning. Sure enough, the movements of the deer, obviously clumsy, caused the arani to somehow lodge itself into its huge antlers. At this, the magical deer did what most deer with aranis in their antlers do – panic. It bolted deep into the forest with the blocks wedged snugly in its antlers. The Brahmin then beseeched his neighbours, the five brothers, to help retrieve the fire-kindling blocks, without which he could not possibly light a fire, which was necessary to make fire-based offerings to the gods.

The Tiresome Chase and the Thirsty Pandavas

At first, the Pandavas weren't sure if they should leave Draupadi alone in the wilderness to chase the deer. But when squarely chided by her for not helping the poor Brahmin, the brothers left her behind in the cottage post-haste, and gave chase to the deer, which managed to disappear into the thicker part of the forest.

Morning turned into noon and noon into late afternoon, and the Pandavas were still panting and puffing after the deer. In a while, their stamina gave way, and utterly exhausted, the princes sat under a shady tree trying to catch their breath, frustrated that a mere deer had defeated them thus far, and that they had succeeded neither in fetching any relief for the poor Brahmin, nor in impressing their beautiful wife. (Why are wives so difficult to impress, anyway?) Sitting dejectedly, Bhima and Arjuna started reliving the insults and injustices suffered by them at the hands of the wily Kauravas. In their beat-up mood, the two pugnacious brothers repeatedly cursed themselves for all those opportunities they had missed – of avenging the many insults their cousins had heaped upon them, particularly the deep affront on the very person of their beloved Draupadi. Had they wrested their due by force then and there, they would not have had to rough it out in forests for a dozen years.

Sensitive to the gloom, and the cause of their miseries, noble Yudhisthira tried to cheer up his brothers, telling them the worst was behind them and that the future could only get better from here. Sensing their dark mood, he also tried defending himself, saying he had been *forced* to accept the challenge of the game of dice thrown at him, in the best royal tradition. He, Yudhisthira, was a rather competent player, and their miserable plight was only on account of dice-sharping by Shakuni, but for which he would have won. In any case, now that they had nearly completed the twelve difficult years in the forests, the thirteenth one was sure to breeze past.

Finally, he asked Nakula to climb the tree under which they were sitting and scout for a possible source of water close by, partly because their throats were parched and partly because anything seemed a good enough diversion when compared to the sullenness of his siblings.

Agile Nakula was up the tree in no time and looked around, the palm of his right hand shading his eyebrows, while the left held a thick branch. He spotted dense foliage almost immediately, not far away. Nor did he miss the animals and birds hastening in that direction – a sure sign of a waterhole in the vicinity. This, Nakula duly reported to Yudhisthira, who asked him to hasten to the source of water, quench his own thirst, and bring back water for them all.

Ah, the demands made on the youngest born! Obedient Nakula picked up a couple of leather quivers to fill with water on the way back, and headed straight towards the thick foliage. He soon came upon a lovely, calm pool, whose water shone under the bright sun like a sheet of shimmering gold.

The Mighty Yaksha

His thirst now redoubled at the sight of pristine pure water, Nakula was about to dip his cupped hands into the pond when he heard a booming voice, clearly that of a yaksha: 'Halt, you trespasser! This pool belongs to me. You may quench your thirst, but only after you have answered my questions!'

Taken aback and stopped mid-action, and not used to being addressed thus, hot, sweaty and tired Nakula was both irritated and unsettled. In any case, no harm would be done if he just had a sip or two of water before attending to this impudent yaksha. So thinking, he continued to immerse his broadly cupped palms into the pool. But no sooner had he done so that he was rendered unconscious, and he fell curled up by the bank of the pool.

The four brothers were getting fidgety at Nakula's delay. Before long, Yudhisthira despatched Sahadeva, the next sibling from the bottom in the pecking order, to check out what was taking Nakula so long. So Sahadeva marched the same route, assured, no doubt, that he would forthwith have his own thirst quenched and return with water for his brothers, with Nakula in tow.

Sure enough, Sahadeva reached the same spot, by the same route and was charmed by the sight of the same scenic pool before he noticed his dear younger brother lying on the bank of the pool, all but limp and lifeless.

What! Who dare treat one of the Pandavas thus? Surely the miscreant or miscreants should be punished forthwith! But let me attend to my punishing thirst first.

Just as he was dipping his hands into the water, he too was challenged by the yaksha. Sahadeva too met the same fate when he disregarded the call in haste and anger.

Arjuna and Bhima followed suit more or less in identical fashion, albeit with progressively increasing belligerence and fluster, no doubt, as they saw two and then three of their dear brothers laid low by some unseen villain, only to be laid low themselves.

The Quiz Prodigy Saves the Day

Now Yudhisthira, completely unnerved at the disappearance of his four courageous and valiant brothers, and no less overcome by thirst, made for the spot himself. As he beheld four of his brothers stretched out on the bank of the pool – the beguiling ambience of which made little impression upon the distressed eldest brother – the usually unflappable Yudhisthira was rattled. It took but a moment for him to realize that this simply could not be the task of an ordinary man, mortal, or even a minor god. This had to be the handiwork of someone remarkably powerful.

Who could have felled his four mighty brothers? No amount of racking of brains provided a suitable enemy. So Yudhisthira did some quick backward thinking. Whoever killed his brothers had to be a mightier warrior or power than his brothers. Clearly, his brothers must have directly defied this mighty and powerful being, and that must have been the cause of their undoing. Clearly, if he was too good for Bhima and Arjuna, he had to be far too good for himself. So clearly again, a straightforward approach to this powerful being would not work. And if the being was so powerful, it was best to humour him and stay alive as long as possible. That would be the only redemption.

But even so, he had to quench his killing thirst first.

And predictably, he was challenged by the commanding voice, delivering the same peremptory message. No less valiant than any of his brothers, even if somewhat less skilled in wielding arms, Yudhisthira certainly carried a more cool head upon his shoulders and stopped mid-action and answered the challenge politely, inquiring, 'Sir, who may you be?'

'The yaksha that owns this pool and the one who laid four of the Pandava brothers low. The fifth one will be no trouble either, should you disregard my warning!'

'What do you want of me, O sire?'

'Only that you first answer my questions before you quench your thirst.'

Yudhisthira, who preferred words to swords, realized that the wisest course would be to follow the track his brothers had chosen to abandon or vice versa. Who knows, he might well survive and live to avenge the plight of his dear dead brothers another day. So he responded, 'All right, hidden yaksha, you may ask your questions.'

The being subjected Yudhisthira to some rapid-fire questions, essentially relating to dharma (righteousness) and ethics. Nobody knows for certain what those queries were, but Yudhisthira, the noblest and most honourable of kings, responded to all of them with a flair and conviction that pleased the yaksha. Received wisdom tells us that the questions and answers may have been in the following vein:

Yaksha: What or who is weightier than the earth?

Yudhisthira: One's mother.

Yaksha: What or who is taller than the mountains?

Yudhisthira: One's father.

Yaksha: What is nippier than the winds?

Yudhisthira: The mind.

Yaksha: What is more numerous than sand particles on a beach?

Yudhisthira: One's worries.

Yaksha: By renouncing what does one become lovable?

Yudhisthira: One's pride.

Yaksha: What, when renounced, makes one happy and wealthy?

Yudhisthira: Avarice and desire, in that order.

Yaksha: Which enemy is invincible?

Yudhisthira: Anger.

Yaksha: Which disease is incurable?

Yudhisthira: Covetousness.

Yaksha: What is true happiness? What is the greatest path?

Yudhisthira: To have no debts; the path of dharma.

Yaksha: What is the best possible bath?

Yudhisthira: Cleansing of the mind of all impurities.

Yaksha: What is ignorance?

Yudhisthira: To be unaware of one's dharma.

...

Resurrection of the Dead

Delighted at Yudhisthira's spontaneous responses, the yaksha allowed him to quench his thirst. And then, as a special favour, he offered to revive one of his brothers. In less than the blink of an eye, Yudhisthira asked for Nakula to be brought alive.

'Nakula? Why not valiant Arjuna or mighty Bhima, who may be far more useful to you in your inevitable fight against the Kauravas? Don't you think this particular response is rather hasty and ill-conceived? Why didn't you take your time responding, O Yudhisthira?'

'Great yaksha,' replied Yudhisthira. 'Of all your questions, this required least reflection. My response is so well considered that no amount of time spent on it can improve it. Of the five of us brothers, three were born to Kunti and two to Madri. To a mother, there is no greater tragedy than the loss of her sons in their prime. For Kunti, there is the consolation that, of her three sons, at least I am alive. Don't you agree that Mother Madri too should be spared the loss of *both* her sons? Surely no other action would be more righteous? Do you really think taking more time to reflect upon your question could have yielded me happiness greater than abating my mother's sorrow?'

'Great Yudhisthira, you are truly the most righteous of them all. Your reputation is well deserved. I had intended to test your values as much as I had meant to issue a lesson in humility to your somewhat impetuous brothers. That is why I arranged for this elaborate charade. Here, I give you back all your brothers! May you accomplish all your goals and be ever-victorious in war,' said the yaksha.

So Yudhisthira's backward logic and out-of-the-box thinking saved the day.

The Lock with the Impossible-to-insert Key

Now take a look at the lock in Figure 32a. It looks innocent enough – just a calm lion sitting on its haunches, its tail doubling as the shackle. As calm as the pool must have looked to the Pandavas. The device reveals its keyhole as obviously as the pool revealed its water.

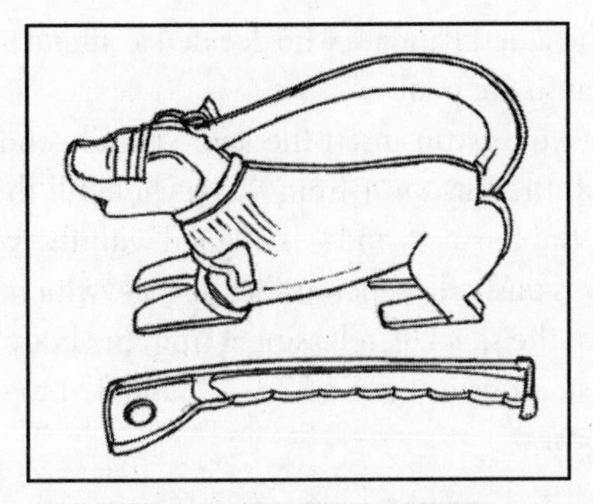

Figure 32a An old bronze lock from Aligarh; no matter how you try to insert the key into the visible keyhole, it cannot be inserted as long as you hold the key by the handle (10.5 × 8.5 × 2.5 cms)

One is as keen to open the lock as the Pandava brothers were to quench their thirst, and the keyhole is as available for one to insert the key directly as the pool was to the brothers to dip their hands into. But if one tries, the efforts will be thwarted, just as the brothers' were. The key simply wouldn't enter the keyhole, even though both the key and the keyhole are genuine, just as the brothers couldn't quench their thirst, even though the water in the pool and the hands that were dipped in it were real enough. There is something as magical and frustrating about the lock and the key, as about the yaksha and the enchanted pool!

You can hold the key by its handle and try to insert it repeatedly into the keyhole, but your attempts would be doomed to failure just as brother after Pandava brother was laid low when each of the four used the same tack.

If you wish to succeed, you will need to hold back, contemplate and come up with a fresh plan – in short, think laterally – like Yudhisthira. Perhaps you need to attack the problem in the reverse order, like the eldest Pandava who decided to attend to the yaksha first and then to the pool.

In other words, you insert the key – handle-end first – and pull it out all the way *away* from the keyhole till the other end of the key – the business end – is aligned with the keyhole, and then the key is pushed deeper inside the lock, which compresses the springs of the shackle, releasing it from the body of the lock. See the illustrations in figures 32b, 32c and 32d to see how the lock functions.

Figure 32b The key is to be inserted into the keyhole, handle first

Figure 32c The key is pulled out through the open keyhole all the way back as shown here, before it can be inserted into the keyhole, as shown in Figure 25c

Figure 32d As the key is pushed in, the shackle is pushed out
(10.5 × 8.5 × 2.5 cms)

Not All Problems in Life Can Be Tackled Frontally

Now why does this remind me of certain class of mathematical problems? Consider the following.

Let us assume that three friends, Amba, Ambika and Ambalika, with a history of much give and take amongst them in the past, find a treasure – a box full of bejewelled ornaments. The three grab a handful each, leaving nothing in the box. From here on, sharing the trinkets involves some complex exchanges. Let us say that in the final analysis, first Amba gave Ambika and Ambalika as many jewels as each of them already had. Next, Ambika gave Amba and Ambalika as many jewels as each of them already had. Lastly, Ambalika gave the other two as many jewels as each of them already had. At the end of all this give and take, each had eight jewels. So how many ornaments had each of them managed to grab from the box of jewels initially?

Before you proceed any further, do try to find the answer on your own. All your direct attacks on the problem are bound to be somewhat frustrating. As you grapple with the problem, trying to tame it by brute force, starting at the beginning, you would soon realize that it is quite slippery and intractable. It remains so unless you try working it backwards, like the key we just described.

You proceed rearward, starting with the final position, thus:

	Amba	**Ambika**	**Ambalika**
Number of jewels with each woman in the last round	8	8	8
Thus, Ambalika must have given Amba and Ambika half of their eight jewels.			
Hence, number of jewels in the second-last round	4	4	16
Thus, Ambika must have given the other two half of their four jewels.			
Hence, number of jewels in the second-last round	2	14	8
It follows that Amba must have given Ambika and Ambalika half of their fourteen and eight jewels respectively.			
Therefore, number of ornaments each of the women grabbed from the box in the first round	13	7	4

Problem Solving: Strategy of Working Backwards

The world of mathematics is full of problems that are not easy to solve with a frontal attack. Even in higher mathematics, there are problems in modern mechanics, system and control theory, etc. which will defeat you if you try to tackle them the conventional way.

The strategy of working backwards involves beginning with the end result and traversing backwards the steps you need to take to get those results, so as to arrive at the solution to the problem.

Such a situation may arise in typically two categories of problems:

1. If the end result is already known and you are trying to find the initial conditions. This situation is identical to what we found in our problem involving Amba, Ambika and Ambalika. Another example is when an auditor reconstructs the accounts of the day, working from the ending cash balance and the vouchers for all the transactions that were made during the day.
2. The category of 'routing' problems, in which one needs to find an optimal route between a point of origin and destination. In this type of problem, the destination is unique, while there are several possible routes from the origin to the destination. In such situations, the strategy of working backwards from the destination enables one to determine the optimal route more easily. Imagine you are in a new city, trying to figure out the best route from the airport to your hotel. You are likely to do better if you first figured out where in the city your hotel is located on the map and then traversed the route backwards to the airport.

Backward induction is a standard procedure for a large number of problems in logic, as we shall see in Chapter 10. The equilibrium solutions for many game-theoretic situations are also found using the same logic.

Often in mathematics, it helps greatly to remove the context of tricky problems from the context of the type of equation that will solve them. In other words, the problem perhaps belongs to a different genre than what you thought it did. Clearly, had Yudhisthira gone along the same lines against the yaksha's challenge as his brothers, he would have failed. And that's why the lion lock defeats you – because it does not belong to your standard genre of locks where you have the key and you see the keyhole, and all you've got to do to get the lock to yield is to insert the key into the keyhole and push or turn. That tactic trounces you when that's not how the key is to be inserted.

In short, there is more than one way to bell the proverbial cat. Try it frontally, or work the other way around.

SEVEN

ABHIMANYU, THE ONE-WAY LOCK AND THE SPACESHIP FROM THE MOON

Chakravyuha

The Pandavas completed their years in exile, albeit not without some divine sleight of hand by Lord Krishna, friend and mentor of the Pandavas, during the thirteenth year. However, when they returned from the jungles, predictably, Duryodhana seemed in no mood to oblige them, dismissing them summarily as losers who had not only gambled away their riches and their wife, but had also cheated on the conditionality of their last year of exile using Krishna's guile. As he refused to give them even as much land as 'could be balanced on the tip of a needle', the Pandavas had no option but go to war. The West may think the first mighty war ever fought was as late as 1914; but we in India know well that it was the war of Mahabharata – fought between the Kauravas and the Pandavas some 5,000 plus years ago, lasting eighteen days – that was the first great war ever fought.

It was the thirteenth day of the war, the day after the grandsire, Bhishma, the generalissimo, had fallen in battle. Guru Dronacharya had taken charge of the Kaurava army and had arranged his army in a battle formation known as the chakravyuha or circular formation.

Now, it is important that you know what this formation is all about. As the name gives some clue, and as is described in the text of the Mahabharata, the chakravyuha is a formation of seven concentric rings of soldiers which keep rotating around the centre. The arrangement is difficult to break through as the soldiers in the ring are constantly moving and do not present an easy target to an attacker. In short, in this formation, one's enemy is constantly changing – imagine a batsman facing a new bowler with every single ball. What is more, as the enemy soldier breaks his way in, the circle quickly closes behind him. And now the enemy soldier is in a pickle, being attacked from both sides – an inner and an outer circle – and is trapped hopelessly inside, like a bee lost within the folds of a carnivorous flower.

To win the battle of the day, the Pandavas simply had to breach the chakravyuha. There existed a unique strategy to breach the formation, and another to get out of it. Of those present in the battlefront, only Arjuna and Krishna knew both the strategies. Krishna was prohibited from direct participation in the war and Arjuna was unavailable. There was one other person, Abhimanyu – Arjuna's incredibly brave son, all of sixteen – who had knowledge of the chakravyuha. The knowledge, alas, was exactly 50 per cent. He knew how to *breach* the vuyha, not how to exit it safely.

Abhimanyu: From the Baby in the Womb to a Valiant Soldier

How this came about is thus. Once, Subhadra – Krishna's half-sister and Arjuna's wife – was suffering heavily from pregnancy blues, especially as Arjuna was away. Krishna, in order to humour a depressed Subhadra, pregnant with Abhimanyu, was trying to distract her with some war stories. The little foetal genius, all snugly curled up in his mother's womb, intently listened to the stories. Just as Krishna finished telling her about the complex chakravyuha formation and how to break into it, he found that Subhadra had dozed off, at which point he stopped telling the story. Consequently, Abhimanyu's education on the chakravyuha remained incomplete and he never learnt how to exit from the battle formation.

Under the Mahabharata treaty, Krishna could not engage in direct warfare against the Kauravas, and was obliged to limit his role to that of Arjuna's charioteer, while his entire army fought on behalf of the Kauravas. So, if the chakravyuha was to be torn asunder, the deed had to be done by Arjuna. But since the Kauravas knew this, they had cleverly orchestrated a large contingent of force under the charge of Sursarma of Trigartas (of the Samasaptakas[1]) to engage Arjuna well away from the main battlefront.

Bhima was the Pandava general on this day, and deployed Yudhisthira to lead a concerted Pandava charge on the chakravyuha formation. But Yudhisthira was thwarted by the spirited counter-attack of Drona leading a padmavyuha or lotus formation. Drona's arrows frustrated every move of the Pandavas, leaving Yudhisthira at the end of his tether.

In the absence of Arjuna who was diverted by the Samasaptakas as planned, and witnessing his uncle's desperation, Abhimanyu offered to lead the assault to break into the chakravyuha formation. However, he informed his eldest uncle that while he knew how to make his way in, unfortunately he had not learnt the strategy for the way out of the formation.

Yudhisthira was hesitant to send someone so young into such mortal danger, and yet he did not have too many options. Besides, Bhima assured Yudhisthira that he would guarantee the safety of the boy, since he himself – along with other mighty warriors like Satyaki, Drupada, Kuntibhoja, Virata, Shikhandi, Nakula, Ghatotkacha and others – intended to escort the brave lad and ensure his safety. To Bhima, life had always been simple: if you could get in, you could get out. So why couldn't they use the same strategy that would get them in to get themselves out as well? This seemed like a reasonable logic.

Abhimanyu Wreaks Havoc

Thus Abhimanyu led the charge, protected by the leading generals of his side. Duryodhana was safely ensconced at the centre of the chakravyuha, with mighty warriors like Jayadratha, Dronacharya, Salya, Karna, Sakumi, Ashwatthama and Kripacharya, and many others in other layers of the rings.

Mighty Jayadratha, the king of the Sindhus and Dhritarashtra's son-in-law, was guarding the outermost ring. Before he could say 'Dhrishtadyumna' – not a very long name by the standards of those times – Abhimanyu had broken through the formation. But the moving circle of soldiers immediately sealed the breach, as if consuming Abhimanyu, and Bhima and the others were unable to crack open even the outermost circle. From then on, Abhimanyu was on his own. He spotted Drona, thanks to his golden-hued flag with the symbol of the ascetic's bowl and a bow fluttering atop his chariot, and made straight for it. The Kaurava army set upon him like fleas on a lion. However, before Abhimanyu, they perished like the same flies in a forest fire. Abhimanyu wreaked havoc upon the enemy, and though he was set upon by several of the Kaurava generals, jointly and severally, he stood his ground heroically. If the Kaurava generals felt any shame at this blatant violation of the rules of combat the two sides had agreed upon at the outset, they did not let the sentiment inhibit their charge unduly. After all, war conditions do not usually engender great respect for rules, and the Pandavas on their part had taken liberties with the rules themselves.

Left beyond the outermost ring, the Pandava generals were launching a desperate and determined onslaught upon valiant Jayadratha to breach the ring – to little avail.

The Slaying of Duryodhana's Son

Deep inside the formation, Abhimanyu was engaged in direct combat with Duryodhana. Drona and other generals came to Duryodhana's rescue once again, and whisked him away. The lad was disappointed at Duryodhana's getaway and vented his anger at anyone who dared cross his path. He fought Kripacharya, Dushasana, Karna and many other Kaurava heroes one-to-one, and put them to flight and shame. The Kaurava army was dispirited and disheartened seeing its mighty generals flee before the young son of Subhadra. Duryodhana's son, Lakshmana, a gallant young warrior, tried to stem the tide by blocking the unstoppable Abhimanyu, who was like a man possessed. But he too soon fell to one of Abhimanyu's lethal arrows.

It is Truly Said: Half Knowledge Can Be Dangerous

A hush descended upon the Kaurava side. Duryodhana let out a scream as only a father who has lost his son in the prime of youth can, never mind that he himself had been trying to kill the equally young son of Arjuna through much of the day. But even a distraught Duryodhana was sentient enough to realize that Abhimanyu knew only half the trick – the way to crack *open* the chakravyuha. Not one to addle his conscience with the finer rules of warfare at the best of times, he commanded Drona, Kripacharya, Karna, Ashwatthama, Kritavarma and Brihatbala to launch a simultaneous attack on the tired Abhimanyu. They cut off the reins of his horses – an act forbidden by the laws of war. They broke his bow by throwing a shaft from behind – another violation of the laws of warfare. They killed his charioteer – another contravention. They shattered his chariot – ditto. Drona, Kripa and Ashwatthama were probably ashamed of doing so, but overwhelmed by the mighty Abhimanyu, they probably saw no other way to stop him. Besides, they were incessantly being goaded by Duryodhana. Thus disabled and overpowered, Abhimanyu fought wielding one of the wheels of his chariot. But he was soon set upon by Daushasani – Dushasana's son – in a mortal combat, and was killed when he was down on his knees.

That Abhimanyu knew his way in, but not the way out of the chakravyuha is the key message of the thirteenth-day battle of the Mahabharata, not unlike this lock I want to tell you about, which I picked up in Gujarat long ago.

The Key That Closes the Lock Does Not Open It

You see an open padlock with a key inserted in the keyhole. You enter your home opening the padlock on your door. However, when you are leaving your home, you find that you are unable to lock the door back. You try twisting the key this way and that; you turn the lock around to spy some secret lever or button; you try savaging the lock using the key – just as Abhimanyu must have tried every trick in the book to get out of the chakravyuha, and in your case, your home – to no avail. And then you are more or less spent, just as Abhimanyu was. This is simply because the key that opened this lock cannot close it. And if you are armed only with the key that opens the lock and not the one that locks it back, you are somewhat like our Abhimanyu, able to enter but unable to exit your abode.

Perhaps they used this lock over a century ago, so your maid could lock the house and get out, but not have a re-entry authorization in your absence. The access to your house remained with you. This lock is shown in Figure 33. Note that there is only one keyhole on the lock and there are two keys. The key shown on the left opens the lock, while the one on the right closes it.

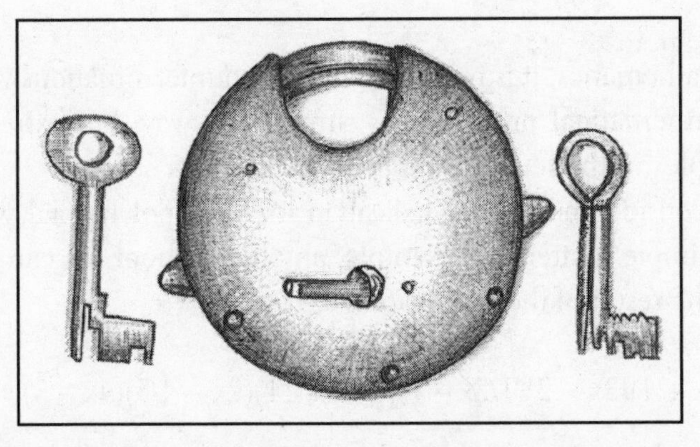

Figure 33 A rare and old lock from Rajasthan/Gujarat/Aligarh, with two keys and a single keyhole; one key closes the lock and the other opens it (15.5 × 13 × 3 cms)

Another variation of this lock was shown in Figure 24 in Chapter 4, in which the lock had two keyholes and two keys, one each to open and close the lock; but otherwise the lock had a function very similar to this one.

Travelling between the Moon and the Earth

Abhimanyu may as well have been a moon dweller who decided to make a visit to the earth using a rocket. Say, he carries enough rocket fuel for the journey, to and fro, hoping he would return the same way he came. Except that when he reaches the earth, he finds there is no way he can get back home, because he didn't realize that earth's gravity is six times stronger than the moon's. To his dismay, he finds he needs way more fuel for the return journey than he did to get to earth. He has the key to enter the earth's atmosphere, but not the one to exit it. Surely an Abhimanyu-like situation.

The One-way Worlds in Mathematics

In mathematics, it is not unusual to encounter situations where a mathematical procedure is simple one way, but extremely complex in the reverse direction.

Consider multiplying radicals to arrive at a polynomial, which is a simple matter. For example, any high-school kid can work out the result of the expression:

$$(x + 4)(3x - 2)(1/2x - 7)(3/4x + 11)(2x - 4/5)(4x - 3) = ?$$

But try factorizing the equation $8x^6 - 26x^5 + 18x^4 + 6x^2 + 4x - 12 = 0$.

It is the same in matrix algebra. You can multiply two suitable matrices, but factoring matrices is a game in another park, so to speak.

Or take a Rubik's cube – the 3-D combination puzzle – scrambling which is simple enough. However, unscrambling the cube back to the original ordered state is a different ball game – er ... a cube game, aw ... never mind. It is not unlike irreversible processes in thermodynamics. Abhimanyu might as well have broken a glass hoping to put it back as easily by a process of simple reversal.

Mathematicians like Martin Hellman and Whitfield Diffe have put in considerable efforts to develop mathematical procedures which are easy to perform in one direction, but not in the other. These processes have been used extensively in coding of messages, which are extremely difficult to decode, which is exactly like giving someone the key to lock a padlock without giving them the key to unlock it.

The One-way World of Calculus

A parallel phenomenon is frequently encountered in calculus as well. For instance, it might appear that if you know differentiation, you should be able to integrate a function merely by reversing your steps. This is mostly true. For example, if $y = ax^n$, where x and y are independent and dependent variables respectively, a is a constant, and n is a real number, then its first derivative dy/dx is given by the expression:

$$\frac{dy}{dx} = anx^{n-1}.$$

By simple reverse logic, applying the usual rules of integration to the function $dy = an\, x^{n-1}\, dx$, integral of the function is given by the expression:

$$y = \int anx^{n-1}dx = a\,\frac{n}{(n-)+1}\,x^{(n-1)+1} + c = ax^n + c \qquad \ldots \quad (1)$$

where *c* is any constant.

Clearly, the integration is the reversal of differentiation and vice versa. This is mostly so, but not always. Let us consider the differentiation of a logarithmic function, like $y = \log_e x$ (where $\log_e$ stands for natural logarithm, which is also expressed as *ln*, and *x* and *y* are independent and dependent variables, respectively).

To differentiate this function, let us go by first principles. A small incremental change δx to the independent variable *x* results in a small incremental change δy to the dependent variable *y*, so that we have:

$$y + \delta y = \log_e (x + \delta x);\ \text{Or } \delta y = \log_e (x + \delta x) - y = \log_e (x + \delta x) - \log_e x$$

$$\text{or } \frac{\delta y}{\delta x} = \frac{\ln (x + \delta x) - \ln x}{\delta x} = \frac{1}{\delta x}\log_e \frac{x + \delta x}{x} = \frac{1}{\delta x}\log_e (1 + \frac{\delta x}{x})$$

As $\delta x \to 0$, lt of $\log_e\left(1 + \frac{\delta x}{x}\right) \to \left(\frac{\delta x}{x}\right)$, so that:

$$\text{when } \delta x \to 0, \text{ lt of } \frac{\delta y}{\delta x} = \frac{dy}{dx} = \frac{1}{\delta x}\,\frac{\delta x}{x} = \frac{1}{x}$$

However, when we apply the rule for integration to the function $y = \int \frac{1}{x}\,dx$, simple reversal (as in Equation 1 above) no longer seems to work. For example:

$$y = \int \frac{1}{x}\, dx = \int x^{-1}\, dx = \frac{1}{-1+1} \text{ x} \times {}^{-1+1} + c = \frac{1}{0} + c,$$

which is infinity!

Clearly, the standard rule of integration does not take us to the expected result, namely $y = \log_e x$. This seeming contradiction arises from the fact that in these processes, we are not dealing with numbers but with limits.

It so happens that the integral of 1/x is inextricably linked to the logarithmic and exponential functions, and unless this is factored into the integration process, it is not easy to arrive at the desired result. The simple process of reversing one's steps does not work.

Exponential functions are typically encountered when we consider, for example, compounded interest growth. Exponential growth occurs when, for instance, we compound the interest for a smaller and smaller time interval. As we continue to compound interest for smaller and smaller time intervals, the interest rate keeps growing, but by a smaller and smaller fraction, thus reaching a limit, which in turn gives rise to exponential functions involving *e*, whose value tends to 2.71828…(To understand the nature of the exponential function, see Appendix 1. It is the same *e* that was at the base of the natural logarithm.)

Now, consider an exponential function: $x = e^y$.

We must have $dx/dy = e^y = x$ (because the derivative of an exponential function is the exponential function itself).

Therefore, $dx/x = dy$, integrating which we get:

$$\int \frac{1}{x}\, dx = y + c, \text{ where } c \text{ is a constant.}$$

However, as $e^y = x$, taking the natural log of both sides, we must have:

$$y = \log_e x$$

$$\text{or } \int \frac{1}{x}\, dx = \log_e x + c.$$

This is what we had set to prove, namely that differentiation (dy/dx of $\log_e x$ is 1/x and integral of 1/x is $\log_e x$ (never mind the constant, which only describes the position of the function and not the function itself).

Clearly, the integration of the function does not turn out to be as straightforward as differentiating it.

It is the same with scrambling an egg, which is easy; but try unscrambling one.

Verily it is said, half knowledge, or just having the key to lock a lock, can leave you out in the cold.

EIGHT

'ASHWATTHAMA KUNJARAHA', FRACTIONAL LOCKS AND KEYS, AND FRACTALS

Generalissimo Dronacharya

The eighteen-day Mahabharata war was in its final phase. The Kurukshetra battlefield was littered with the bodies of soldiers, horses and elephants, not to mention, shattered chariots and weaponry. The surviving soldiers, horses, elephants and undamaged chariots were rushing pell-mell over and around the carcasses and ruin. Soldiers and stalwarts alike competed keenly to get their bows and lances into the chest of their opposite numbers, with each missile that found its mark being cheered loudly by its side. More and more bodies were piling up. Vultures flew high in the sky, knowing the end of the day, or feed time, was nigh.

The Kauravas had lost Bhishma, Bhagadatta, Bhurisrava, Jayadratha and a great many of Duryodhana's ninety-nine brothers, and many more. Among the Pandavas, Arjuna's son Abhimanyu, Bhima's son Ghatotkacha, and a great many others had laid down their lives in the epic war to help the Pandavas secure their share of the kingdom. Some might have wondered that while it may have been the Pandavas' dharma (as driven home by Lord Krishna) to fight for their kingdom, there was no moral compulsion for the hundreds of other kings on either side to indulge in the wanton killing since it was not their kingdom that was at stake. Clearly, even if the thought had come, it might have been too late.

It was now the fifteenth day of the epic war. Dronacharya – the great Brahmin-teacher of Kauravas and Pandavas alike – was now the generalissimo of the Kauravas, after the death of the great Bhishma. Stung by their latest losses – of Bhurisrava and Jayadratha – no sooner had he taken charge, Drona had let loose all his fury and skill upon the Pandava army. Also castigated by Dhritarashtra and Duryodhana as being a traitor for not fighting his best on account of his affection for the Pandavas, the ageing guru was wreaking indiscriminate havoc upon the Pandavas like a tsunami. Such was the old Brahmin's fury that he was on the verge of letting loose the Brahmastra – the then equivalent of the nuclear warhead! Should he release the ultimate missile, it would be the end of the Pandavas and their cause, and much else besides. All their efforts to fight for righteousness would come to naught. And once the Brahmastra was released, it would simply complete its catastrophic deed, leaving little for the Pandavas to do in defence or counter-offence.

The Dirty Plot

Worried on all these counts, Yudhisthira and his brothers retreated into a dejected state of mind, when their wily strategist, Krishna, suggested a tactic of dubious virtue to salvage the situation. It was well known that ageing Dronacharya held his son Ashwatthama – a youth of great valour and virtues – dearer than life itself. Killing Ashwatthama, given the immediate exigencies of the state of war, was not feasible. But if Dronacharya could be convinced that Ashwatthama had been killed, the news would so thoroughly demoralize the old man that he would lose all enthusiasm, energy and reason for living, and all fight would be drained out of him, whereupon killing him would be a relatively simple exercise. The plan was shocking to all those who listened to Lord Krishna – the god himself! But Krishna convinced them that given that Drona was invincible under the standard rules of warfare, it was alright to take a teeny detour around righteousness. Moreover, allowing Drona to release the Brahmastra would spell large-scale devastation, killing many, many more, while telling a minor lie would prevent that devastation, and kill only the wielder of that terrifying weapon. Krishna justified the action on the strength of the fact that in order to uphold higher dharmas – of fighting for your legitimate rights, and preventing the Brahmastra from being discharged – a lesser dharma, like an act of cheating, may have to be committed. Extraordinary times call for extraordinary interpretations of the rules of ethics, right and wrong! Moreover, the choices on offer in life are often grey, rather than black or white. Perhaps the lord was underscoring this lesson.

The Fractional Truth and the Death of Drona

Possessed of the strength of a thousand elephants and armed with his massive mace, Bhima took upon himself the relatively simple task of slaying a Kaurava elephant that trumpeted to the name of Ashwatthama. Having killed the elephant, he announced – in a mighty roar, aided by the strength and power of Lord Hanuman's vocal chords (remember the 'old monkey'?) – that he had slain Ashwatthama.

Hearing Bhima's call, Drona looked at him with disdain, convinced about the invincibility of his incredibly brave son, and asked Yudhisthira if Bhima's bragging about slaying Ashwatthama was true indeed. Clearly, the old teacher believed that Dharmaputra Yudhisthira, the very personification of righteousness, could speak no lie – not even for all the kingdoms of the earth and the heavens. Dharmaputra, torn between his venerable teacher's expectations of his truthfulness and the larger objective of the war, saluted the ageing and former teacher, and replied, 'Ashwatthama hathaha iti, narova kunjaraha', meaning, 'Ashwatthama is dead ... but as to whether it was a human or an elephant, I am not sure', the latter part of the sentence being murmured softly. Wily Krishna drowned the qualification of his statement by blowing hard on his conch shell at exactly the right moment. This in turn triggered loud and joyous beating of drums by the Pandava army, which, combined with the anguished din of the Kaurava army as it heard of yet another of its great heroes being slain (like the anguished din we heard from Indian fans every time Sachin Tendulkar failed to score his 100th hundred), ensured that Guru Drona never heard the latter part of Yudhisthira's statement.

Yudhisthira's endorsement was enough to plunge the great Drona into deep gloom. All vitality drained from him; he lost all will to go on, and withdrew into himself, laying aside his bow, arrows and other assorted arms in an unthinking haze. And this is when Dhrishtadyumna, Draupadi's brother, whose family nursed an old enmity against the guru, to the horror of all who witnessed the act, mounted the acharya's chariot and slew him.

For upholding one good, another good had been forsaken. For the prevention of one evil, another one had been committed. So what's right, and what's wrong? Was Yudhisthira's statement to Drona true or false; his action honourable or dishonourable? We all understand what is right and what is wrong. The difficulty we encounter is not when we have to choose right from wrong, but when the choice is between two rights or two wrongs, or from among shades of grey, as in the case above. For example, we all know that telling lies is wrong. But suppose we are in an alien land where the host cooks a laborious meal for us, taking pains to understand our palate, and it turns out we didn't quite like the meal as it was not cooked the way we like it, should we tell them the truth when they ask us how we liked the meal? Is the truth the right thing to utter when it may hurt the gracious host? Is lying such a bad act under the circumstances? 'Ashwatthama is dead' is the truth. But with the latter part being deliberately drowned in the sounds of war-drums, the whole statement is rendered a partial truth. Is it a half-truth? Or more than half, but less than the full truth? If killing people is wrong, is the body count in war justifiably right? If only partially right, how much? So, are there fractional truths? Do we have fractional rights and wrongs? Do we have a truth–falsehood duality at play?

Fractional Keys?

We have so far encountered locks that call for one or more than one keys. Take a look at the one in Figure 34a. How many keys does it have? Is it just one key, or two, three, four keys? But before you answer, you need to know more about this lock.

You see a key and a sharp pin-like wire. True, this pin has a function in opening the lock, but the fact is, you can use any pin for the purpose and not necessarily the one you see. But the catch is, try as you might, you will find no obvious pin-hole in the lock in which to insert the pin. And had the pin not been given to you, you would have no reason to believe that you even need a pin to serve any function. So is this pin really a key? Or is it a fraction of a key?

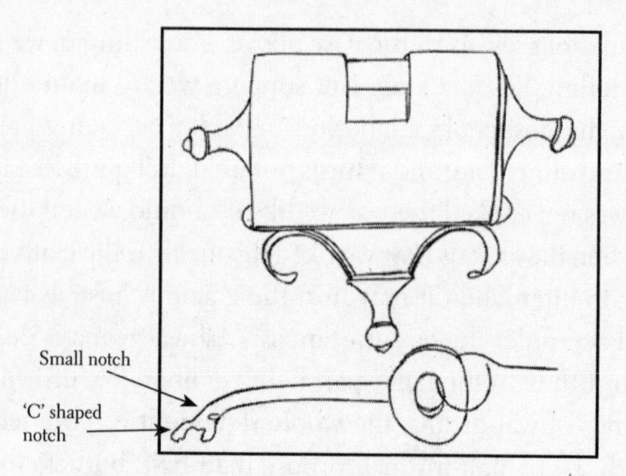

Figure 34a A rare and unusual lock, probably from Aligarh, with a key and a pin (any pin would do) (5 × 12 × 2 cms)

But yes, there is a minute chink on the side of the lock that looks like any chink where metal parts usually meet, and there are several such chinks all over the lock, as you will shortly realize. When this pin is inserted into one of these, it presses a spring that releases the shutter at the bottom of the lock to reveal a slat with four rotatable floral dials (see Figure 34b).

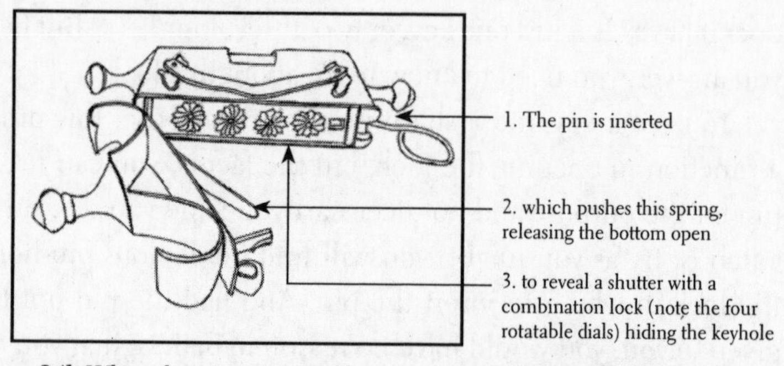

Figure 34b When the pin is inserted into a minute hole on the side as shown, the bottom of the lock swings open, revealing a shutter locked in place through a combination lock (the floral dials on the shutter can be seen above)

Now, knowing where to insert the pin is a knowledge that is also a 'soft key'. So do we add this knowledge as another key?

And yet, the lock is far from open. The slat conceals the actual keyhole, being held in place by the four rotatable dials which form a combination lock (Figure 34b) – a sort of lock within a lock! Each of the floral dials has seven alphabets etched onto it, and you need to get each dial in a certain position to open the hatch. So then, the combination code of these dials represents yet another key. Is it more than one key now ... or is it a fractional key again? Ergo, once you have the combination in place, the keyhole is revealed, and the lock looks like this.

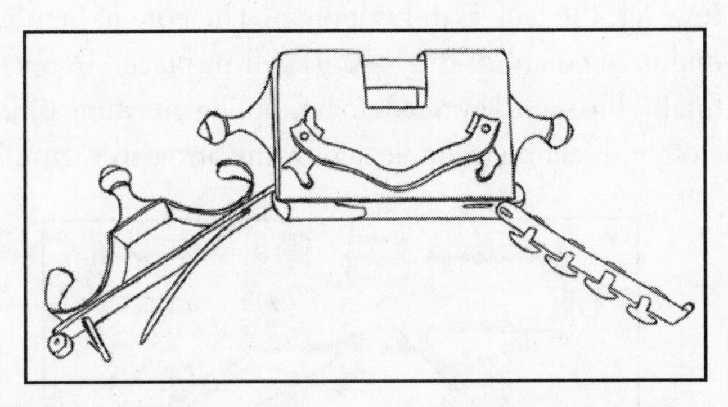

Figure 34c As the combination is applied, the shutter opens as shown

You now apply the main key (shown in Figure 34a), working it in one direction (as shown by the arrow mark in Figure 34d) to remove the outer casing of the shackle.

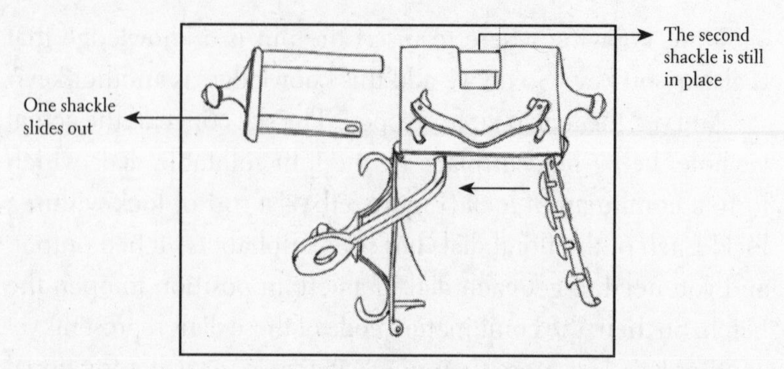

Figure 34d The main key when inserted and pulled from right to left, slides out one of the shackles (which is telescoping into the main shackle on the right) towards the left

However, the lock is still not open. The core of the shackle (top-middle segment of the lock) is still in place. To open the lock finally, the same key needs to be applied one more time, but in the other direction (as indicated by the arrow in Figure 34e).

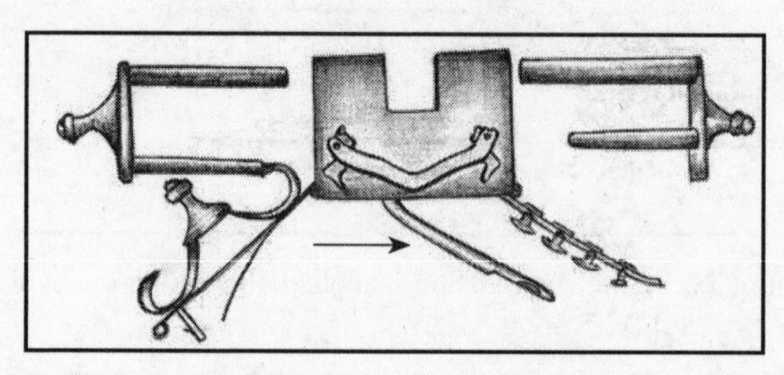

Figure 34e The same key is applied in the reverse direction and pulled from left to right for the main shackle to slide out on the right

Figure 34a shows two notches in the main key. There is one main notch at the end, curved like a 'c' and another small one on the top-right side of the main notch. These are the two working notches of the key, and each shackle (the left shackle is tubular, and encases the right shackle) is worked through the two different notches of the key. Thus, the main key is two-keys in one! So, in all, how many keys have we applied to open our lock? 3, 3.5, 4, 4.5, 4.7, 5.2, or more?

And this analogy takes us to fractals, or fractional dimension, which is a dimension suspended between two whole dimensions.

Take a look at the lock in Figure 35. How many keys does it have?

Figure 35 Is this a lock?
(8 × 5 × 1.5 cms)

Each fragment of the key shown, as well as the whole key looped into the shackle, is required to open the lock. But is this really a lock? Well, this is actually a puzzle – a mechanical puzzle designed by a good friend of mine, Dan Feldman of Israel, a former IBM executive, who is among the world's leading puzzle collectors. The objective of this puzzle is to open the lock using the broken pieces of the keys, and then re-assemble exactly as shown in Figure 35 once again. So we have a lock–puzzle duality here – a fractional lock, in a way – since the lock is only partly a lock, and more a puzzle than a lock!

Fractional Dimensions

We understand truth and falsehood. But how true was Yudhisthira's fractional truth to Drona? Over half? Or less than half? Maybe close to full? We understand an object as being either a lock or not being one. But how much of a lock is the fractional lock in Figure 35? We understand a lock opening with one, two or three keys. But how many keys does it take to open the lock in Figure 34a? Or the one in Figure 35? We are suddenly transported to an unusual world, no longer in our familiar zone.

It is the same with the world of dimensions. We all understand the world of a single dimension (a line), two dimensions (a plane), three dimensions (a cube) and even four dimensions (including 'time' to the three dimensions of space). But more difficult to come to grips with is the world of fractional dimensions. For example, what do we mean by 1.6 or 0.7 dimensions? Does it make any sense at all? But that is what the world of fractals or fractional dimensions is all about. Let us try and take a peek into the world of fractional dimensions using some simple examples.

Example 1: Let us say, Line 1 represents a length of twelve inches, Line 2, six inches; and Line 3, four inches. If we were to measure the length of Line 1 using Line 2, we will need two lengths of the latter ($R = 2$), which will split Line 1 into two equal segments ($N = 2$) of six inches each. Similarly, if we measured Line 1 using Line 3, we will need three lengths of the latter ($R = 3$), which will divide Line 1 into three equal segments ($N = 3$) of four inches each. At the moment, you may think N and R are more or less the same thing; but they are not, as you will see once you go past Example 1.

Example 1: Dimension (D) = 1 (because this is a line).

1. ____________

   N = 1

2. ______ ______

   N = 2, R = 2

3. ____ ____ ____

   N = 3, R = 3

So far so good. No major challenges to our intellect here, like the simple truth that a leaf is green, or that our plain vanilla locks can be opened using the key provided, as long as the keyhole is unambiguous and easy to locate.

Example 2: Now consider the square in Figure 36a, in which each side represents twelve inches. The square has two dimensions, so that dimensions (D) = 2, while we have one square (N = 1).

Figure 36a N = 1

Using a six-inch scale (R = 2), the above square (Figure 36a) may be broken into four equal segments (N = 4), each a 6" × 6" square, as shown in Figure 36b. The difference between *R* and *N* should now become clearer.

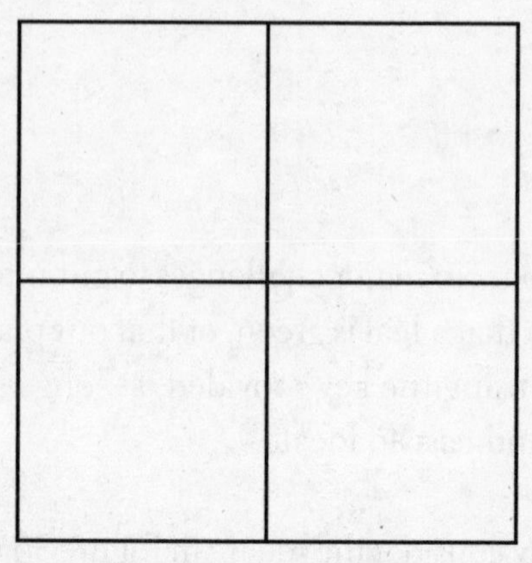

Figure 36b N= 4, R = 2 (each side being six inches)

Using a four-inch scale (R = 3), the square in Figure 36a may also be broken into nine equal segments ($N = 9 = 3^2$), each a 4" × 4" square, as shown in Figure 36c.

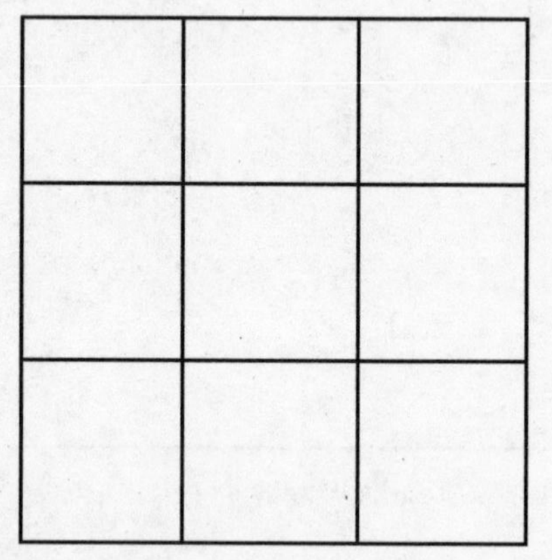

Figure 36c N = 9, R = 3 (each side being 4 inches)

Again, we are in safe territory, like a slightly more complex truth that leaves are green except in autumn, or that you may be presented with locks with two different keys, which do not present us any great challenge of familiarity or comprehension.

Example 3: We now extend the same logic to a cube. Consider the cube below of dimensions 12" × 12" × 12", so that the number of dimensions (D) = 3.

Figure 37a shows that when R = 1, N = 1; in Figure 37b, we see that when R = 2, N = 8 = 2^3; and in Figure 37c, it is evident that when R = 3, N = 27 = 3^3.

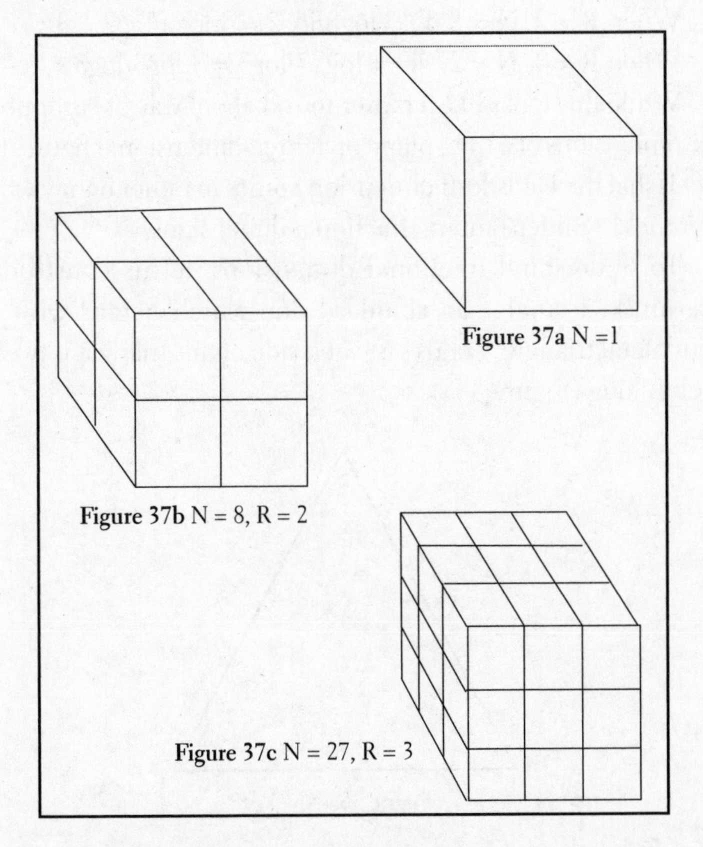

Figure 37a N =1

Figure 37b N = 8, R = 2

Figure 37c N = 27, R = 3

Now, Felix Hausdorff, a German mathematical astronomer defined dimension – called the Hausdorff dimension – thus: $N = R^D$, or $D = \log N / \log R$. Let us see how good this holds true.

It can easily be seen that in Example 1, irrespective of the value of *R* and *N*, since the two are always equal, the value of D turns out to be 1.

In Example 2:

When R = 2, N = 4, D = log4/log2 = 2 log2/log2 = 2,

When R = 3, N = 9, D = log9/log3 = 2 log3/log3 = 2.

Similarly, in Example 3:

When R = 2, N = 8, D = log8/log2 = 3 log2/log2 = 3,

When R = 3, N = 27, D = log27/log3 = 3 log3/log3 = 3.

While this looks like a rather round-about way of computing the dimensions of a line, plane or a three-dimensional figure, the fact is that the Hausdorff dimension comes in rather handy when it comes to understanding fractional dimensions.

To understand fractional dimensions, let us construct a Sierpinski triangle – a standard one which begins with an equilateral triangle. Let us say, each side of this triangle is twelve inches long (Figure 38a).

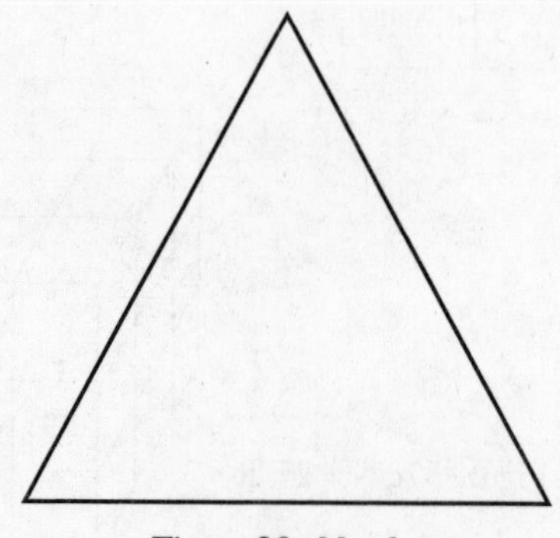

Figure 38a N = 1

We now connect the midpoints of the three sides to create three identical equilateral triangles (N = 3), so that each side of the three triangles is six inches (R = 2) long, with the three smaller triangles making point-contacts to create a fourth triangle which is actually a hole (represented in black), as shown in Figure 38b.

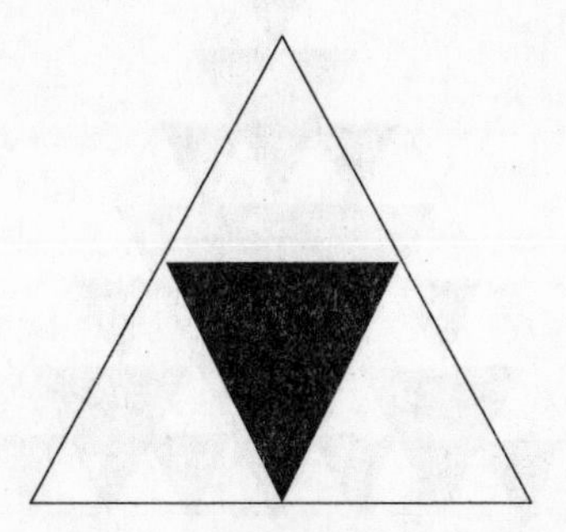

Figure 38b R = 2, N = 3

Sierpinski Triangle

Let us repeat the above process in each of the triangles. We now get nine identical white equilateral triangles (N = 9) joined at the points (as numbered in Figure 38c) in clusters of three, each side being three inches long (R = 4).

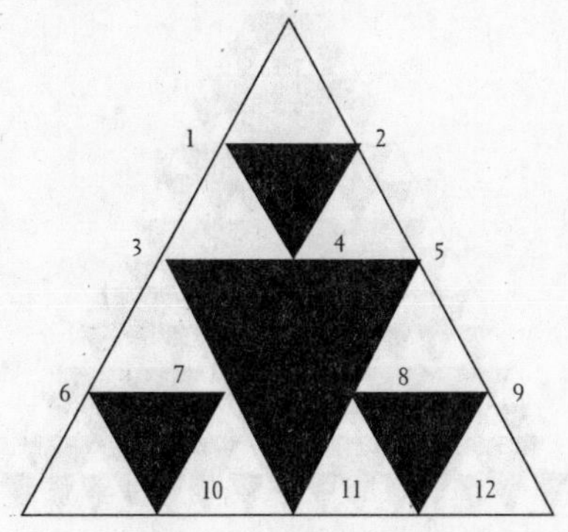

Figure 38c $R = 4 = 2^2$, $N = 9 = 3^2$

As we carry on with the same process once more, we get twenty-seven smaller traingles, so that we have $R = 8 = 2^3$ and $N = 27 = 3^3$, as seen in Figure 38d.

Figure 38d $R = 8 = 2^3$, $N = 27 = 3^3$

If we iterate yet again in the same manner as before, we get a system of eighty-one traingles, all making point contacts, with the black spaces always representing the holes, so that we have $R = 16$ and $N = 81$, and so on (Figure 38e).

Figure 38e $R = 16 = 2^4$, $N = 81 = 3^4$

So in order to form the Sierpinski triangle or Sierpinski sieve, we keep repeating the process infinitely, and the number of little triangles, both white and black (holes) keep getting smaller and more numerous. It should be noted that it is not possible to physically construct an actual Sierpinski triangle, because to be able to do so, one has to keep dividing each side of the triangle into smaller and smaller segments an infinite number of times (increasing the R indefinitely), which is not actually possible. Incidentally, counter-intuitive as it may sound, in order to obtain a Sierpinski triangle, it is not necessary to start with a triangle. Mathematically, it is possible to obtain a Sierpinski triangle by starting with shapes other than a triangle as well. So then what is the dimension of the Sierpinski triangle?

This is where the Hausdorff dimension comes in handy, which is simply given by log N/log R which, in all the cases, is nothing but log 3/log 2 or 1.585 ...

In other words, the Sierpinski triangle has a dimension close to 1.6. Intuitively this sounds reasonable, in the sense that the triangle certainly seems to involve more than just one dimension. But is it two-dimensional? Had its dimensions been two, as in the case of a normal triangle, every point in the plane within the boundaries of the triangle ought to have been accessible. However, in case of a Sierpinski triangle, it can be seen that some of the points or spaces are simply out of bounds at any given stage. In this sense, it has a dimension less than two, and the actual Hausdorff dimensionality works out to about 1.6. And yet, a little reflection reveals that the surface area of a Sierpinski triangle is zero! You can work that out using high-school geometry for the area of triangles and some algebra.

Sierpinski Pyramid

We can extend a similar logic to the Sierpinski pyramid, which bears the same relationship to the Sierpinski triangle that a triangular pyramid (which has a triangular base) bears to a triangle. Figure 39a shows a triangular pyramid (a tetrahedron, to be precise), all of whose edges are the same length, say, twelve inches.

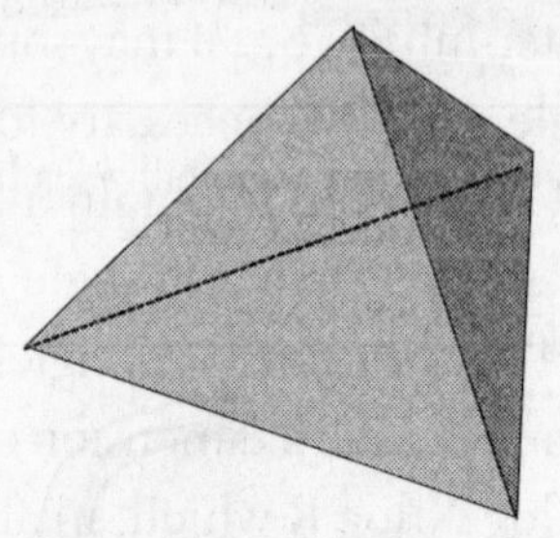

Figure 39a Tetrahydron

To start constructing a Sierpinski pyramid, as a first step, we begin with making smaller pyramids, each of whose sides is of half the length, or six inches (R = 2), each pyramid making only point contact with the others (see Figure 39b). It can be seen that doing so leaves us with four small equal-sized pyramids (N = 4) at the vertices, and four triangular holes in the middle, one showing on each surface as a Sierpinski triangle, as seen in Figure 39b.

We repeat the process with each of the four pyramids, so that each yields four smaller pyramids, making a total of sixteen little pyramids (see Figure 39c). At this stage, we have R = 4 (2^2) and N = 16 (4^2).

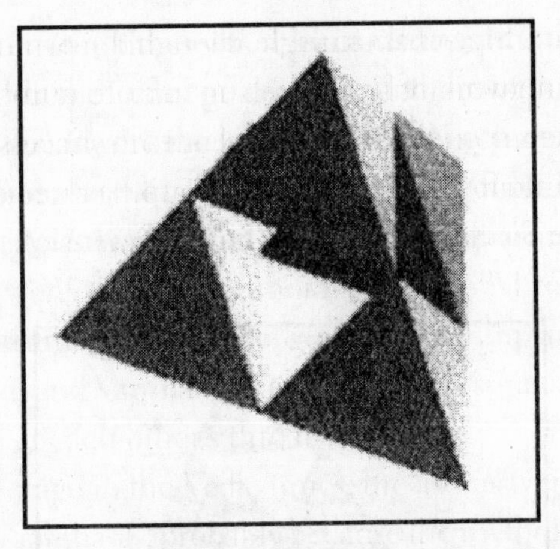

Figure 39b R = 2, N = 4

Figure 39c $R = 4 = 2^2$, $N = 16 = 4^2$

In order to construct the Sierpinski pyramid, conceptually, we need to continue this process indefinitely, until we begin to have a hollowed-out pyramid approximating the structure as shown in Figure 39d. It is easy to see that each face of the Sierpinski pyramid is nothing but a Sierpinski triangle, though the pyramid itself is a labyrinthine network of lines forming infinite number of holes, somewhat like a sponge. As can be seen, each successive pyramid breaks down into four smaller pyramids – like a three-dimensional version of the Sierpinski triangle. Three dimensional?

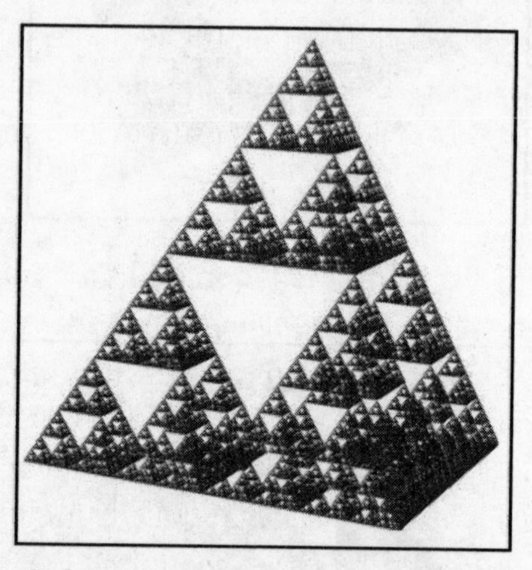

Figure 39d As *R* and *N* get larger and larger, we approach the Sierpinski pyramid

The Hausdorff dimensionality of the Sierpinski pyramid works out to log 4/log 2 (log N/log R), which is simply 2. In other words, a Sierpinski pyramid is two dimensional and not three! And what is more, because the surface area of each face is zero, the volume of a Sierpinski pyramid is zero! This is intuitively acceptable: just as the volume of any plane, which is two-dimensional, is zero, the volume of the Sierpinski pyramid, which is also two-dimensional, is also zero. And yet there is some difficulty in coming to terms with this truth. What is apparent is not factual and what is factual is not apparent.

This is also the nature of truth, like what Drona heard Yudhisthira say. Truth, like fractional dimensions, is often difficult to come to terms with. What appears to be the truth may not be. Alternatively, what is indeed the truth may not be obvious.

Truth can be like the key shown in Figure 40a.What do you see? A key, right?

Figure 40a Is this a key?
(11 × 6 × 1 cms)

A Lock–Key Duality?

What you see in Figure 40a is a lock. Surprised? That's what this lock is all about. Even as you are searching for a lock in the figure, it is right there before you – the lock that looks like a key. But then again, the lock is also a key. Confused?

All right. Take a look at the Figure 40b.The smaller key, when applied to the larger 'key'…er…lock, opens it!

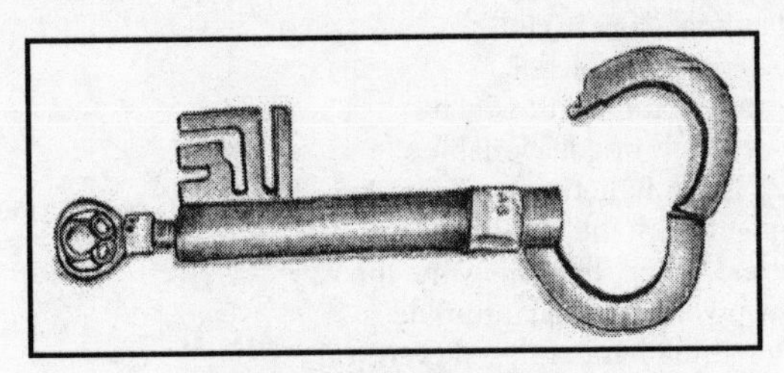

Figure 40b The key lock

And what if the lock in Figure 40b were also a key to the lock in Figure 41?

Figure 41 The lock–key duality
(14 × 10 × 4 cms)

Clearly, we would have a lock and key duality on our hands, like Shikhandi, who was instrumental in killing Bhishma, and was both male and female at the same time!

You could say that Schrödinger's cat (see a charming little poem on it*)[1] – which is both alive and dead – is like Yudhisthira's

*Cecil, you're my final hope
Of finding out the true Straight Dope
For I have been reading of Schröedinger's cat
But none of my cats are at all like that.
This unusual animal (so it is said)
Is simultaneously live and dead!
What I don't understand is just why he
Can't be one or other, unquestionably.
My future now hangs in between eigenstates.
In one I'm enlightened, the other I ain't.
If you understand, Cecil, then show me the way
And rescue my psyche from quantum decay.
But if this queer thing has perplexed even you,
Then I will and won't see you in Schröedinger's zoo.

statement to Drona, which is in a state of limbo between truth and falsehood.

Duality in Boolean Algebra

The world of mathematics is full of dualities – double-duality, self-duality, dual spaces, De Morgan duality or the duality principle; duality in linear programming, etc.

While a detailed discussion on dualities is beyond the scope of this book as well as its author, here is a window into the duals in the world of mathematics, with the example drawn from Boolean algebra.

The basic operations inherent in Boolean operations, namely, *and*, *or* and *not* (conjunction, disjunction and negation) mimic multiplication, addition and complement, respectively, in ordinary mathematics. For example, some authors use the same arithmetic operations as ordinary algebra reinterpreted for Boolean algebra, treating xy as synonymous with $x \wedge y$ and $x + y$ with $x \vee y$.

Conjunction: Operation $\wedge$ behaves on 0 and 1 exactly as multiplication does in ordinary algebra. $x \wedge y$ implies that if both x and y are 1 then, $x \wedge y$ is 1, but if either x or y is 0 then $x \wedge y$ is 0. In other words, $x \wedge y = xy$.

Disjunction: Operation $\vee$ mimics addition, but not quite. For instance, $x \vee y$ works thus: if both x and y are 0, then $x \vee y$ equals 0. And if either x or y is 1, $x \vee y$ equals 1. However, $x \vee y$ is not 2, when both x and y equal 1. This may be represented by $x \vee y = x + y - xy$.

Complement: This operation is equivalent to negation in regular mathematics, in that it replaces or interchanges values. However, negation in regular algebra is flipped around 0, while negation in Boolean algebra is flipped across the midpoint of 0 and 1, as it were.

To explain further, in ordinary algebra, negation interchanges 1 and –1, 2 and –2, and so on, leaving 0 fixed. However, in Boolean algebra *complement* interchanges 0 and 1. This is represented by $\neg x = 1 - x$.

The above rules of operations may be summarized as:

$$
\begin{array}{lcl@{\qquad\qquad}lcl}
0\wedge 0 &=& 0 & 0\vee 0 &=& 0\\
0\wedge 1 &=& 0 & 0\vee 1 &=& 1\\
1\wedge 0 &=& 0 & 1\vee 0 &=& 1\\
1\wedge 1 &=& 1 & 1\vee 1 &=& 1\\
\neg 0 &=& 1 & \neg 1 &=& 0
\end{array}
$$

The standard values of the symbols of Boolean algebra are 0 and 1. However, there is nothing unique about the choice of the symbols for these values. For example, if we could consistently rename 0 with ϕ and 1 with γ, our algebra would remain unchanged, except for some minor differences.

But what if we replaced 0 and 1 with 1 and 0, respectively? Such replacement, even though the algebra would remain Boolean, would no longer be identical to the Boolean algebra that we are familiar with. For example, in our new system, $1\wedge 1$ must equal 1, while in the original Boolean algebra, this ought to have been $0\wedge 0$, which would have been 0.

We may now ask, what happens if, in addition to interchanging the names of the values, we also interchange the nature of the two binary operations. The resulting algebra is rendered identical to our original algebra, since the interchanges nullify the effects of each other completely.

When values and operations can be paired in a manner which results in status quo when all the pairs are interchanged simultaneously, the member of each pair is called a dual to each other. Thus, the values 0 and 1 are dual, and so are operations $\wedge$ and $\vee$. According to De Morgan duality or the duality principle, Boolean algebra remains unchanged when all dual pairs are interchanged.

A similar phenomenon of duality is evident in accounting. If you merely interchanged the symbols debit (dr) and credit (cr), the resulting accounts will not be the same as the original. However, if, at the same time as interchanging the symbols, you also reverse the nature of the transactions, you will get the original accounts intact.

Wave–Particle Duality

This is not unlike light exhibiting properties of waves and particles at the same time. When physicists first began to study light, they saw it behave like an electromagnetic wave and so deployed the mathematical properties of waves to understand it better. Now, waves come with certain unique mathematical properties, which require specific methods of analytical treatment. For instance, we have the transverse and longitudinal waves whose motion is typically to be understood as wave function, but whose properties in turn depend on things like the wave amplitude, frequency, period, speed, wavelength, pulse, etc., all of which together yield the wave equation (the exact composition of which the reader is best spared).

In subsequent years, other observers discovered that light also exhibits particle-like properties. In other words, light also seemed to be made up of discrete particles, or rather, discrete bundles of energy or designated photons, such that any single photon had a fixed, distinct energy level. It was also seen that the intensity of visible light could be increased or decreased only by changing the number of photons present. This particle-like behaviour seemed perfectly consistent with the basic property of light to travel in a straight line. Being electrically neutral, photons would indeed travel in straight lines, without being affected by electro-magnetic fields.

But it soon became evident that if photons were to be particles indeed, we would run into trouble explaining some of the observed behaviour of light. For instance, when light enters a dense medium from vacuum, like, say, entering our planet's atmosphere from the vacuum of space, it slows down, as it ought to. However, it surprisingly maintains a constant speed through the atmosphere and does not continue to slow down as it keeps moving, which, if it were made of particles, it must, on account of friction. Similarly, when light moves from a denser medium to a less dense one, it picks up speed again, and holds constant again – something that ordinary laws of physics do explain.

After this, it was realized that photons were not exactly particles, but simply electromagnetic waves that also exhibited particle-like behaviour. This would explain why and how a photon could transfer its energy to an electron – known as the photoelectric effect – as in a high energy-photon shoving an electron to a higher orbit around the nucleus or even entirely off the surface being struck. When this happens, the electron holds that energy for a while before falling back to its original lower-energy orbit and, in the process, releases the energy absorbed. This effect has not only been observed experimentally, but been put to good use – such as in photomultipliers (light-sensitive vacuum tubes), and image sensors of the early days of televisions, etc.

In short, here was the realization that photons were waves and particles at the same time and therefore exhibited the properties of the two. But the mathematics for waves and mathematics for particles are not the same. So, mathematically, how does one manage this duality? Clearly, special techniques were needed for the purpose.

It was De Broglie who may be said to have risen to the challenge. He was perhaps the first one to come out with the mathematical formulation of quantum mechanics by using precise mathematical construction of wave–particle duality of photons and electrons in 1923. This branch of mathematics, using infinite-dimensional Hilbert spaces and operators on these spaces, and what have you, is distinct from the mathematical formalisms for theories that were developed before the 1900s, which were largely dependent on differential geometry, partial differential calculus, and the theory of probabilities and statistical mechanics. These theories, though capable of handling the complexities inherent in the theory of relativity, could not handle the demands of quantum mechanics.

The truth–falsehood duality in the Mahabharata, the lock–key duality in the world of padlocks, the mathematical duality in Boolean alegebra or the wave–particle duality in physics – they all seem to have a surreal likeness, helping us explore the world of unexpected parallels.

NINE

THE SCORPION BITE OF KARNA, SCORPION LOCKS AND BAYESIAN SEARCH FOR THE USS *SCORPION*

Look at the kaleidoscope of scorpion-shaped locks below. Each is different from the other, not only in appearance but also in the way it works. Some of them – for example, the one shown in Figure 42a can actually hurt you if you are not careful. The same lock is shown in Figure 42b with the limbs, claws and tail folded in. This lock, as also the one shown in Figure 43, has pointy and movable limbs, and if you do not have the correct key and are fooling around with the wrong one, unable to grip the lock properly, you are likely to injure your hand.

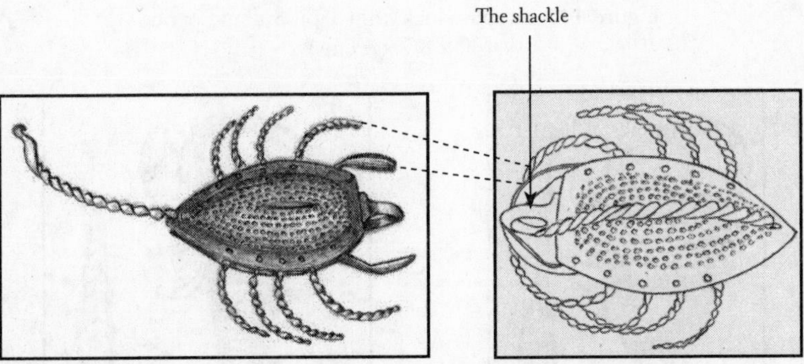

Figure 42a A spiky scorpion, with pointy limbs, claws and tail, which can hurt you seriously if you do not have the right key: (22 × 13 × 3.5 cms)

Figure 42b The tail and every claw and limb of the scorpion can be folded in

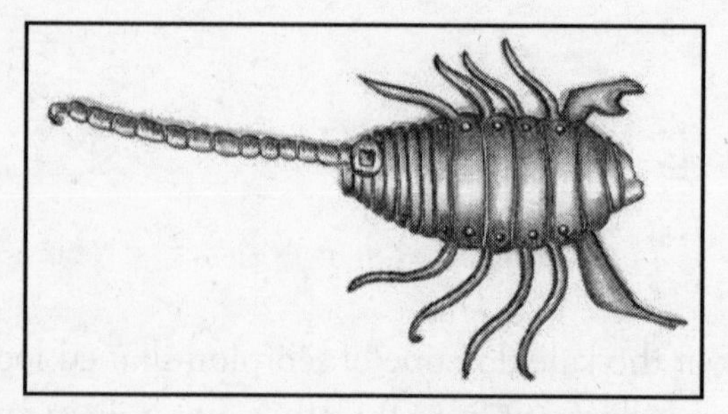

Figure 43 A variant; the shackle cannot be seen because it is positioned under the belly
(18 × 11.5 × 1.5 cms)

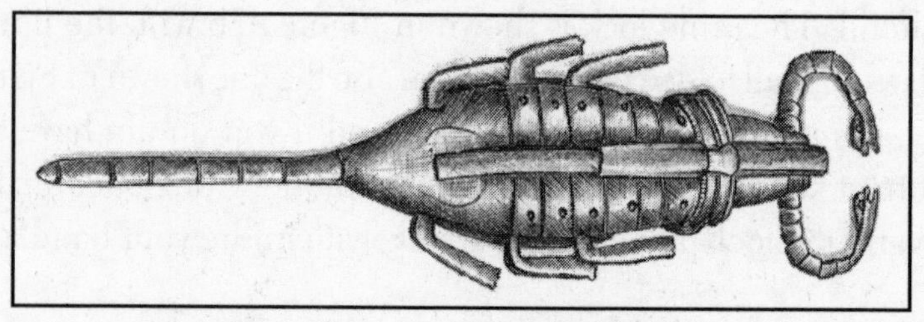

Figure 44 A scorpion lock from Tipu Sultan's period
(30 × 8.5 × 4 cms)

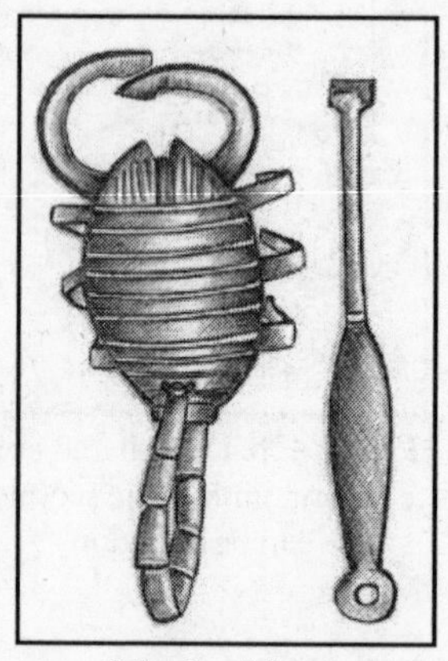

9.5 × 5 × 5.5 cms

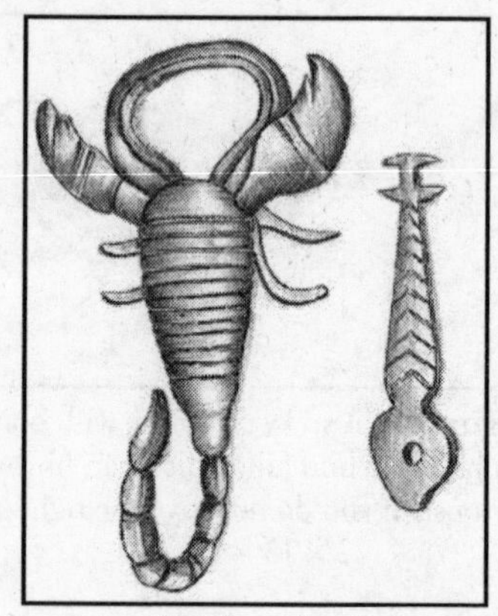

12 × 8 × 4.5 cms

Figures 45 and 46 New locks, typically made for tourists – mostly made in Rajasthan and Gujarat

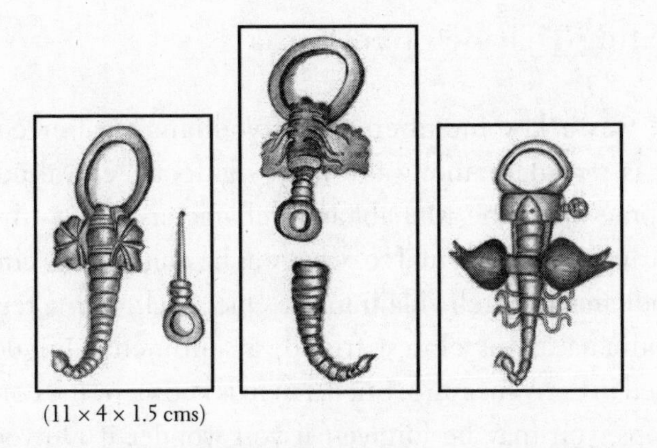

(11 × 4 × 1.5 cms)

Figures 47a, 47b and 48 Rare and old locks – most likely from Aligarh

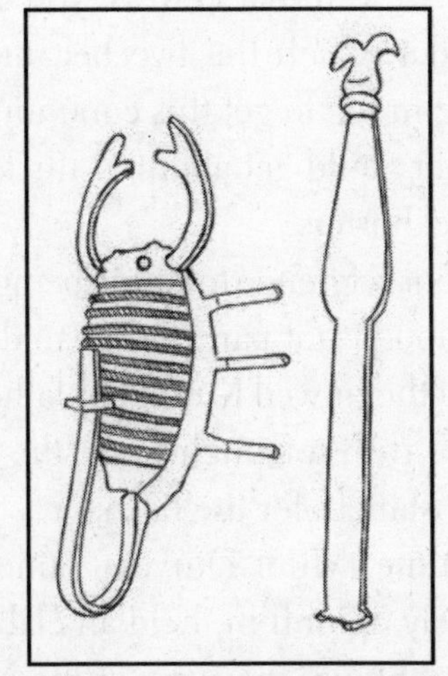

Figure 49 A new, touristy lock from Rajasthan
(14 × 9 × 4 cms)

Figures 43 through 49 show other interesting variants of the scorpion theme. The sheer variety of scorpion locks reminds me that a scorpion plays a key role in the Mahabharata as well. We will need to dig deeper into the epic to see how.

The Sting That Betrayed Karna

Karna was a key member of Duryodhana's inner coterie. Karna is regarded among the most righteous, chivalrous and handsome of all the Mahabharata characters – even more so than Arjuna himself. But if so, what was he doing in the circles of Duryodhana, the arch villain in the epic? Well, Karna regarded Duryodhana as his closest friend, a sentiment Duryodhana returned in every measure. But if a man is known by the company he keeps, you may be forgiven if you wonder if Duryodhana was as bad as the epic makes him out to be, or if Karna was all that virtuous, after all. But that's only if you are unaware of the circumstances under which the two became friends. So let's begin from the beginning to get this conundrum sorted out. Be warned that the plot could get about as thick as the thickest of the Bollywood blockbusters.

You will recall our reference to Karna being the eldest brother of the Pandavas, though not part of the Pandava gang since he was the first born of the unwed Kunti. His father was the sun god himself. Before you rush to conclusions, the epic does provide extenuating circumstances for the birth.

Once upon a time, Muni Durvasa, famed for wearing his temper rather loosely upon him, held an elaborate yajna in the palace of Raja Kuntibhoja, the ruler of the kingdom of Kunti. Kuntibhoja was the foster father of Kunti, who was born as Pritha, and was the aunt of none other than Lord Krishna (being the sister of Vasudeva, Krishna's biological father). She had been given away to Kuntibhoja, by his friend King Shurasena, who was Pritha's biological father, to raise as his own daughter as Kuntibhoja was childless. Aware of Durvasa's extremely irritable disposition,

Kuntibhoja had wisely put the beautiful and gentle princess in charge of taking care of the volatile muni's hospitality. Kunti did such a splendid job of caring for the old sage that a grateful Durvasa taught her a secret mantra which would enable her to summon virtually anyone to her presence at will.

It is understandable that a teenaged Kunti, granted such a powerful mantra as this, tested its potency by summoning none other than the sun god to her bedside, and ended up being an unwed mother – a matter of great shame in those times – even if it was a divine conception and the baby was none other than Karna, a beautiful and radiant infant, complete with a golden armour. With the help of her trusted maid, Kunti put the baby in a basket and cast it away in River Charmanwati. In due course, the child would be found by Adhiratha – the royal charioteer of King Dhritarashtra – and raised as his own son in Hastinapura.

If you have been following the narration closely, you will also recall how Karna was insulted by Draupadi as being the son of a lowly charioteer and therefore not being worthy of her royal hand. Karna had fumed at the jibe but couldn't do much about it.

At another time and another place, another insult had cut him deep; this at the hands of none other than Guru Dronacharya. As the princes Drona tutored were graduating, he held a sort of convocation ceremony in the form of a championship among the princes to showcase their prowess with different weapons. Watching the show from the sidelines, Karna was unimpressed by the simplistic feats of the princes, any of which he could not just match, but better by a goodly margin. It was also clear that the guru was placing far greater weight upon archery if only to project his pet Arjuna as the winner of the show. After all, hadn't the guru not only refused to tutor Ekalavya, a tribal prince, but also called upon the boy to cut off his thumb as guru dakshina (guru's fee) so that Arjuna's supremacy in archery would not be dwarfed by the vastly superior archer that Ekalavya promised to be? And this, when Ekalavya was essentially self-taught and only *considered* Drona his guru! Well, the teacher was not beyond playing politics with a lad young enough to be his grandson, and now he was at it again – such were Karna's thoughts. Arjuna was indeed the best of that lot, but he, Karna, could do any trick that Arjuna could, and then some.

Thus, just as the guru was adjudging Arjuna as the winner of the championship, Karna challenged the call, daring Arjuna to compete with him using any weapon of his choice. He challenged the guru that if he indeed thought Arjuna to be the best in the kingdom, surely he should have no reservations in allowing the third Pandava to pit his talent against him.

Now the wily guru was not unaware of Karna's superiority to Arjuna. But having been the teacher of both the Pandavas and the Kauravas, it would not do to let the most accomplished of the princes lose to the son of a charioteer. It would neither make the king happy, nor enhance his own esteem as the royal guru. So he disparaged Karna in front of thousands of onlookers for his lowly status, reminding him that combatants could only be equals, and that a charioteer's son did not have the locus standi to challenge a prince.

Drona's words pierced Karna's heart like no arrow could, and the insults hurt his ego like no javelin could. It was on this occasion, when Karna was at his most vulnerable, that Duryodhana came to his rescue. Duryodhana perhaps saw this as a good moment to gain the friendship of the mighty and prodigious warrior who might well stand him in good stead as a counter-weight to Bhima and Arjuna combined, should he ever have to fight the Pandavas. Or maybe he just related to Karna's anguish at being denied unjustly the opportunity to display his skills and defeat Arjuna, especially as Duryodhana had little love lost for this particular cousin. Anyhow, the strategic friendship must earn Duryodhana an A+ in strategy in any of today's top business schools.

So the eldest Kaurava gifted Karna the kingdom of Anga, anointing him *Angaraj* or king of Anga, then and there. Now that Karna was king, surely he had earned the right to challenge Arjuna? Whether Duryodhana's move had been chivalrous or calculated, it did not win the argument against Drona, since Arjuna himself refused to accept the challenge from a charioteer's son, anointed king or not. Nevertheless, this gesture endeared Duryodhana to Karna with an affection that would never be diluted. Now Karna had always been a most giving and a generous soul. In time, as he presided over the empire of Anga, he used his wealth for more and more philanthropy. No mendicant would leave his palace disappointed with a wish unfulfilled. As his reputation for charity grew, one could always see a long queue of all kinds of beseechers in front of his palace.

Now the gods, who were largely on the side of the Pandavas, were worried at the friendship between Duryodhana and Karna. For not only was Karna a greater warrior than all the Pandavas put together, the fellow was also born with a built-in body armour, and was hence virtually unconquerable. So if this strategic advantage to Duryodhana was to be neutralized, Karna and his body armour had to be parted, sooner rather than later.

A conclave of gods persuaded Lord Indra, the king of gods, to exploit Karna's philanthropic temperament. The idea was for

Indra to appear as a Brahmin mendicant at Karna's doorsteps and seek his divine armour in alms. Karna, they knew, would grant this and would be rendered immeasurably weaker.

The sun – himself a god, and Karna's father – warned Karna about Indra's intended plan. However, Karna was steadfast on his stand that no supplicant could go empty handed from his doors, even if he were a god in disguise and the charity could eventually cost him his life. And thus, Karna gave away his armour to Indra in alms.

When Duryodhana learnt of this, he was most unhappy, and wanted Karna to seek the Brahmastra from Guru Drona. Karna knew the foolishness of seeking the old teacher's help. However, Duryodhana insisted that now that Adhiratha's son was a king, Drona could not legitimately refuse to have him as his student, and once he did, a warrior of Karna's standing would pass every test required to merit the knowledge of the Brahmastra.

Most reluctantly, Karna approached Drona, only to be insulted as a lowly-born by the guru all over again. This left only one other teacher who held the secret of the Brahmastra – the great sage Parashurama.

Now Parashurama, the great axe-wielding and perennially angry Brahmin warrior, was Lord Vishnu-incarnate, and through great penances to Lord Shiva, was said to have obtained knowledge of all weaponry, including the secret of the Brahmastra. But Parashurama was also a sworn enemy of Kshatriyas and was never happier than when wielding his axe across their throats, nor would he ever accept anyone other than a Brahmin as his pupil. It is this Parashurama that Karna had to turn to if he were to acquire the knowledge of the weapon of all weapons.

Now, Karna was not a Brahmin, and brought up as a

charioteer's son, he was considered low born. However, as Angaraj, he would be deemed a Kshatriya, or the warrior class, and for that reason alone, teaching him would be anathema to Parashurama. So view it as you may, Karna had as much chance of being accepted by Parashurama as his pupil as I may have of ascending the British throne.

Parashurama's abode was atop the Mahendra Mountain in the upper reaches of the Himalayas. It was to this destination that an apprehensive Karna headed. In the ashrama of the great warrior guru, he introduced himself as a Brahmin adept in all forms of weaponry. He also stated his ultimate objective – of acquiring the know-how of the Brahmastra. The old sage, thanks to the dark interiors of his dwelling and his failing eyesight, could not quite make out that the man before him was as much a Brahmin as he, Parashurama, was an apsara.

In due course, the old sage found Karna a great pupil. Karna passed with flying colours every test that the sage subjected him to in order to gauge his eligibility for being given the secret of the Brahmastra. In some time, even this was done and Karna possessed the great secret, which none of the Pandavas had.

It was about this time, one lazy afternoon in the middle of a jungle, when the guru and pupil were sitting under a tree, discussing the nuances of the Brahmastra, when the guru fell asleep. Karna lifted the guru's head gently and placed it on his lap, so that his teacher could be more comfortable. The ageing guru looked tired and in need of his rest.

It had been a couple of hours since Karna had been sitting in that position that a scorpion climbed up his foot and commenced a rapid journey up his leg, tail held high like a flag. Karna fought the tickling sensation of the arachnid walking all over him. As it reached his thigh upon which rested the guru's head, he flinched, lest the insect sting his guru. The flinch was enough for the animal to sting Karna on his thigh. Within moments, the poison started spreading through the blood stream, causing unbearable pain to Karna. But the devoted student did not move a muscle, lest his movement wake up his teacher. His breathing all but stopped, his face puffed up in pain, and his thigh began to bleed.

As the stream of blood ran into the guru's head, Parashurama opened his eyes and took in the scene. Seeing the obvious wound upon his disciple's thigh, the guru enquired why Karna did not wake him up in time. Karna respectfully replied that he did not want to let a mere non-lethal bite from a scorpion to disturb his guru's rest.

One would expect the guru to be touched beyond words at such a caring and dedicated pupil. But not Parashurama. The guru immediately stood up and, looking directly into Karna's eyes, said, 'You cannot be a Brahmin as Brahmins simply do not have the ability to endure pain as you have. You must surely be from the warrior class of Kshatriyas, which means you acquired your knowledge under false pretext, and that too nothing less than the Brahmastra! So here is my curse: just when you need the Brahmastra the most, you will forget the chants to summon it, rendering you incapable of using the ultimate weapon! Now leave, you liar, before I change my mind and let fly my axe upon you.'

And that's how Karna was rendered vulnerable, and could not use the Brahmastra during the Kurukshetra war. He was killed by Arjuna in violation of all rules of fair warfare – when he was off his chariot, trying to extricate its wheel from a ditch. And with his death, it was curtains for the Kauravas, and any announcement of their defeat in the epic war of Mahabharata a mere formality. Duryodhana was avenged by Bhima shortly thereafter. Yes, the Pandavas got their kingdom after all.

The Origami Scorpion That Saves Lives and Mathematics

Does a scorpion find a place in mathematics? Does mathematics find a place in origami? Can origami and mathematics save lives? Now, what's going on here? Well, contrary to what one may imagine, today, a lot of mathematics goes into the ancient art of origami – the art of making objects by folding a sheet of uncut paper. Thanks to modern-day application of folding algorithms developed by mathematicians, the development of a paper scorpion today saves a lot of lives!

How? Ask Dr Robert Lang – an eminent origami artist, designer and engineer from the US – who will tell you that there is a lot modern science cannot do without origami! According to him, science, technology, space, automotive engineering, medicine – all have benefitted greatly from origami. And the art leads to a better appreciation of various mathematical geometric concepts relating to space as well.[1]

And that's how an algorithm which origami artists developed for designing the twists and folds in an origami scorpion led to the algorithm that paved the way to the creases for flattening an airbag in automobiles! In other words, the simulation codes used for the origami scorpion and other insects to develop sequenced crease patterns have now been adopted into airbag simulation code, helping design better airbags!

The Search for USS *Scorpion* and Mathematics

Mathematics and scorpions come together in another unexpected way. US Navy Attack Submarine, USS *Scorpion* (SSN-589), which was lost in the high seas in 1968 while transiting from the Mediterranean to Norfolk, Virginia, was found by applying the Bayesian search theory. Other objects found with the help of the same technique include the space shuttle Challenger in 1986; MV Derbyshire (the largest British vessel ever lost) that got lost at sea in 1980 and was found in 1994; the SS Central America – also called the Ship of Gold, that plied the seas between Central America and the US in the 1850s – that was lost in 1857 and found in 1986; Lucona, an old cargo vessel sunk deliberately for insurance fraud in 1977, in the Indian Ocean, and found in 1991; and most recently, Airbus AF 447 which disappeared mysteriously on 31 May 2009.

But first, let us focus our attention on the USS *Scorpion*.

USS *Scorpion* was a nuclear submarine of the Skipjack class and the sixth vessel of the US Navy to carry the same name. The ship was launched on 19 December 1959.

The submarine saw considerable use in various tactical exercises, winning a Navy Commendation medal in 1966. She underwent a significant overhaul in 1964, and finally, carrying her reputation for excellence as a sharp attack submarine, entered the Norfolk Naval Shipyard for the last and an extended overhaul of its short life in 1967.

As work progressed, for various reasons, the *Scorpion*'s original 'extended overhaul' was pruned down in scope, so that a SUBSAFE programme that had originally been planned, was dropped. This meant that the vessel would go without a central control valve system, meaning that in case of an emergency, the crew would have to run helter-skelter to find and operate the manual valves. The result was a significant loss of morale on the prestigious sub.

Under these circumstances, the *Scorpion* took to the Mediterranean on 16 May 1968 with a new captain and participated in some operations in tandem with the 6th Fleet, and then headed home. During the journey, according to the records, the sub suffered several mechanical failures, alongside a Freon gas leak from its refrigeration system. This was followed by a short circuit in the electrical system, causing a fire. With the situation worsening by May 21, the *Scorpion* tried desperately to send a distress radio signal to the appropriate naval authorities but without success, and was subsequently reported six days overdue in Norfolk.

Navy personnel suspected the worst and a search was launched. By 5 June, the sub was 'presumed lost' with ninety-nine hands on board, and her name struck off the Naval Vessel Register by the end of June.

Enter Mathematics

The search for the *Scorpion* now shifted gear and entered the domain of mathematics. Dr John Craven, chief scientist of the US Navy's Special Projects Division, was brought in to head a team of mathematicians to lead the search. The group brought in the powerful tool of the Bayesian search theory to locate the *Scorpion*. The theory had been fine-tuned earlier while searching for a lost hydrogen bomb off the coast of Palomares, Spain, in January 1966.

How does Bayesian theory help in the search of a lost object like a submarine? The search framework helps one to use all the available information systematically, to deploy probability theory to the search of a lost object.

The Bayesian World

But what exactly is the Bayesian framework? In the Bayesian world, probability measures a degree of belief before and after accounting for all available evidence. An intuitive way of understanding the Bayesian approach is often explained by the well-known precocious baby example. Imagine a newborn Abhimanyu-like baby who observes his first sunrise and wonders if it will rise again. In the absence of any other information, he considers another sunrise to be as likely as not. In other words, he ascribes a *prior likelihood* of 50 per cent to the same event. This is the prior probability. The baby represents the equal likelihood of both possibilities by placing one black marble and one white marble into his bag. Next morning, when he witnesses another sunrise, he adds a white marble to his bag. Now the bag has two white marbles and one black. At this stage, the probability that a randomly pulled marble from the bag will be white is 2/3 (posterior probability), up from 1/2 earlier. Again, the following morning, the child sees the sun rising and adds yet another white marble into the bag, at which time the probability that a randomly pulled marble from the bag will be white is 3/4. Thus, with each unfolding piece of evidence, the child is able to revise its degree of belief about the sunrise. If the baby keeps it up long enough, its initial belief that the likelihood of the sun rising every day is 50 per cent, is modified to the point of becoming a near certainty.

More formally,

If A stands for the proposition and *B* for the evidence:

P(A) represents the *prior probability*, or the initial degree of belief in the proposition,

P(A|B) is the *posterior probability*, is the degree of belief in A, given the evidence B, and

P(B|A)/P(B) is the total support provided by evidence B for the proposition A.

The above principle is deployed with great effect when testing or searching for a disease, phenomenon or even lost objects. It must be understood that tests and events are two different things. For instance, we may test someone for bird flu, which is different from the event of actually having bird flu. We often overlook the fact that tests may not be 100 per cent accurate. A test may be positive for bird flu when a subject does not have the disease (false positive) or may not detect the flu when a subject does have it (false negative).

In this sense, tests give us test probabilities, and not the real probabilities. Test probabilities suffer from the errors in the tests. For instance, we could have:

The test showing positive (test = +ve) when the patient does have the bird flu (bird flu = true) = true positive

The test showing positive (test = +ve) when he/she does not have the flu (bird flu = false) = false positive

The test showing negative (test = –ve) when the person being tested does have the bird flu (bird flu = true) = false negative

The test showing negative (test = –ve) when he/she does not have the disease (bird flu = false) = true negative.

Let us see how the presence of false positives often distorts the results significantly. To understand how, let us take a closer look at someone who has been tested positive. Let us say the doctor tells you that the test administered is an excellent one and known to predict the flu correctly 95 per cent of the times, when you do have it. How worried should you be under the circumstances? Most people will be terribly worried.

The question we ought to be asking ourselves is, given that we have been tested positive, what is the probability that we do indeed suffer from bird flu?

To answer the above question, you need some more background information, namely how common or rare is the bird flu in nature? Supposing it is extremely rare, occurring, say, one in 500. This means that if we test, say 1,000 subjects, we will expect 998 of the subjects to be free of bird flu. Thus, of the two (actually $1.9 = 1000 \times .02 \times .95$) who may actually have the flu, given the 95 per cent accuracy of our test, both the cases may be expected to test positive. In addition, thanks to the false positives, the test will also indicate a positive result in 5 per cent of the 998 cases who do not have the flu. In other words, of the 998 non-flu cases tested, our test will show about fifty cases ($\cong 998 \times .05$) to be positive or as having the flu, and of the two who may actually be suffering from the flu, both will almost always be tested positive. Thus, of the 1,000 cases tested, we may expect a total of fifty-two cases to be positive (about two true positives and about fifty false positives).

Given the above information, the probability that one actually has the bird flu when one has have been tested positive can only be about 2/52, or about 3.7 per cent. Clearly, one has a pretty good chance of being free of the flu!

In formal statistics, it is represented thus:

$$P(\text{bird flu} = \text{True}|\text{Test} = +\text{ve}) = \frac{P(\text{Test} = +\text{ve}|\text{bird flu} = \text{True}) \ X\, P(\text{bird flu} = \text{True})}{P(\text{Test} = +\text{ve}|\text{bird flu} = \text{True}) \times P(\text{bird flu} = \text{True}) + P(\text{Test} = +\text{ve}|\text{bird flu} = \text{False}) \times P(d = \text{False})}$$

$$= \frac{0.950 \times 0.002}{0.95 \times 0.002 + 0.998 \times 0.05} = 0.0019/0.0515 = .03668 \text{ or } 3.67\%.$$

Bayesian Theory in Search Operations

So how does one apply Bayesian principles to the search of lost objects? To deploy Bayesian theory to search algorithms, we first need to develop a set of hypotheses about what happened to the lost object – a submarine in this case. Next, we build a probability distribution around each hypothesis for the possible locations of the vessel. For each specific location, we construct a probability distribution for actually finding the lost vessel in that specific location, given that the vessel is indeed in that location (a distribution of conditional probabilities). For example, if a vessel is lost in deep waters, it may have drifted much farther than if it had sunk in shallow waters, so that the probability distribution in the former case may be much more scattered than in the latter case.

Next, we collate all the probability distributions into a single aggregate distribution, which is obtained by multiplying the two probabilities. This is the probability that we shall find the submarine in a specific location l, given all probable locations. This results in something like a graphic plot of probabilities for all possible locations. We then chart a search path, beginning from the most dense or most probable locations, to least dense or least probable locations. And finally, we keep modifying the probabilities as we continue the search. For instance, when we do not find the sub in a given location, we reduce the probability for that location significantly, while increasing the probabilities to the other locations. The modification or revision is done using the Bayesian framework.

This framework helps us estimate the economic viability of a search for a given probability of success. For instance, at the very outset, the framework can tell us something like, 'There is a 60 per cent chance of finding the sub over a one-week search, which may rise to, say, 85 per cent after a 10-day search and 95 per cent after a two-week search.' Thus the economic viability of the search can be estimated before committing resources to it.

The actual development of the Bayesian probabilities of Dr Craven was much aided by a hydro-acoustic expert – one Gordon Hamilton, who pioneered and deployed this expertise – to significantly reduce the search area; and it was in this vicinity that the drowned *Scorpion* was finally found squatting.

The best-known application of the Bayesian method is also the most recent, involving the search for a lost aircraft, AF 447, which met one of the most mysterious accidents ever in aviation history. The aircraft, with 228 people on board, took off from Rio de Janeiro to Paris on 31 May 2009. Flying over the southern Atlantic, the Airbus met with a high-intensity electrical storm at high-altitude and vanished without a trace, with no survivors.

If the mystery was to be solved, the black box needed to be found. But it is perhaps easier to find the proverbial needle in the haystack than a shoebox-sized black box in the Atlantic. After two years of futile attempts, Airbus resorted to a Bayesian review of their search operations and updated the pre-search information available until then. Now as we saw earlier, the Bayesian rule essentially involves updating initial or prior beliefs with new objective information in order to obtain a new and improved belief. The consulting firm, Metron, ascribed a high probability to the credibility of its data relating to wind speeds, flight path, tidal currents and other information relating to aircraft crashes, and thus was able to narrow down the search area. This process introduced the possibility that the alarm signals connected to the black box for pinging had failed at the time of the crash, which in turn narrowed down the possible high-priority area that the hydro-acoustics or the sonar system may have missed, and within a week of the new search, the wreckage and the black box were found nearly four kilometres under sea on 3 April 2011.

If only Duryodhana had been able to apply the Bayesian algorithm to the search for the Pandavas, he may well have averted the Kurukshetra war by thwarting the condition of incognito living in their thirteenth year!

TEN

SHUKRACHARYA AND KACHA, A PAIR OF INTERACTING KEYS, AND BINARY STARS

A Lock with Interacting Keys

Here is a lock that works with two keys. So what's special, you may ask, having seen quite a few of them by now, including your neighbourhood bank lockers. What is special about this lock is that the two keys interact on each other! How do the keys interact? Check out the keys in Figure 50a below.

While one of the tubular keys has spiral grooves cut on the inside, the second one has corresponding grooves cut on the outside. The first key is inserted from one side of the lock, and the second from the opposite side, coming onto each other. Thus the first key enters the second and is rotated like a screw. This compresses a spring between the two keys in the bowels of the lock, releasing the shackle (see Figure 50b). The two keys are interdependent as neither of the keys can by itself do even a part of the job of opening the lock – like taking us one step closer towards opening the lock as we saw in many of the locks with multiple keys earlier. It is only when they interact upon each other that they open the lock, and in this sense, they form a single key.

Figure 50a The lock with interacting keys from Rajashthan
(8 × 7.5 × 3.5 cms)

Figure 50b The lock opens when the keys interact on each other inside the lock
(8 × 7.5 × 3.5 cms)

And this is where Shukracharya and Kacha come in. The story goes thus:

Suras and Asuras at Loggerheads

The Mahabharata has hundreds of side stories, looping one into the other. Here is one of them.

Those were the times when humans are said to have shared the earth with the suras or devas, and their half-brothers, the asuras. The devas were the lower gods, and included Indra (king of the gods and also the god of weather), Agni (fire), Usha (dawn), Surya (sun), Apas (water) and Yama (god of dharma and death). The asuras were the gods of morals, such as Mitra (the god of contract), Aryaman (guardian of guests, friendship and marriage), Bhaga (share) and Varuna (sky and wind).The suras and the asuras were always at each other's throats.

At some stage in the Vedic times, the asuras were turned into demons, or raakshasas, probably because the mythological history came to be written by the suras. While Sage Brahaspati was the patron guru of the suras, the guiding spirit of the asuras was Shukracharya who, incidentally, was also the son of Sage Vyasa, the author of the epic Mahabharata and the biological father of Dhritarashtra and Pandu. Shukracharya, through is meditation and invocation of higher gods, had obtained the secret of Sanjivani, the secret mantra that could bring the dead back to life, thus providing the asuras a vibrant public health system. (It warrants caution that the reader distinguish Sanjivani the secret mantra from the herb with the same name that, eons ago, Hanuman had set out to fetch when another demon, Meghanada, Ravana's brother, had laid low Lakshmana, Lord Rama's brother, in a duel.) The monopoly over the Sanjivani gave a great advantage to the asuras over the suras whenever the two squabbled and killed each other, which was more or less customary for the two sides. No matter how many asuras the suras killed, Shukracharya would bring them back to life. The number of devas began to dwindle, creating a population gap between the two warring parties that one could drive a chariot through. This was clearly an alarming situation for the devas.

Our gods then, as even we mortals are today, were nothing if not scheming. So an elaborate scheme was brewed in the camp of the devas. The plot, in brief, devised by the sura guru-in-chief, Brahaspati, was to get his son Kacha to worm his way into the sanctum of Shukracharya as his student, win his confidence, learn the secret of the Sanjivani, and bring it back to the devas.

Kacha did as bid. As it transpired, before long, Kacha had also wormed his way into the heart of Shukracharya's comely and eligible daughter, Devayani. Devayani fell in love with Kacha who in turn saw considerable strategic advantage in reciprocating her affections for the leverage it would provide him in wheedling out the secret of the Sanjivani from her learned father.

The asuras – demons though they be – were no fools. With their flaring nostrils and strong gut feel, they could smell Kacha's nefarious designs a mile off. To ensure that they would keep their secret, they promptly killed the spy who was romancing their guru's beautiful daughter. Besotted in love, a distraught Devayani beseeched her doting father to bring Kacha back to life by use of the Sanjivani. This Shukracharya did. Thereupon, this became a tiresome routine. The asuras would kill Kacha time and again, each time taking care to make smaller and smaller pieces of him, to the point of virtually making minced meat, or rather a paste, of his dead remains and dissolving it in the ocean. But doting fathers being doting fathers, each time, Shukracharya was prevailed upon to bring Kacha back to life by Devayani's pitiful entreaties.

Finally, the asuras had had enough. So this time they killed Kacha, burnt his body, dissolved his ashes in wine and served it to Shukracharya himself on a quiet evening. And this time, as Devayani pleaded with her ever-obliging pater to bring Kacha back to life, the boring routine suddenly got interesting, as realization dawned that they had a tricky situation on hand.

As Shukracharya tried to use the Sanjivani to bring Kacha back to life, nothing happened, at least not on the surface. Instead, he heard a faint rumbling and gurgling emanating from his innards, as if he had partaken of sumptuous quantities of boiled cabbage. Clearly, Kacha had been reassembled in his bowels but was imprisoned inside Shukracharya. He was now trying to speak out, the attempt at cogent speech bubbling forth as a rumble. In this imprisoned state, Kacha narrated to Shukracharya how he had landed up in the latter's stomach.

Shukracharya was beside himself with rage and began cursing alcohol and its consumption in equal measure. Nor did he spare those whose brainwave it had been to serve the beverage. He then briefed Devayani of the predicament, informing her that she would have to choose between Kacha and himself, because if Kacha was to be saved, he (Shukracharya) would have to perish, as Kacha had no option but to tear his stomach to come out. Alternatively, his stomach would be Kacha's permanent dwelling place.

Devayani doted on her father as much as she was besotted with Kacha. Neither would do by himself, just as neither key by itself would do to open the lock we referred to in Figure 50a.

But love and reason usually go in opposite directions. What is more, children of big shots then, as today, rarely accepted 'no' for an answer in our land. Devayani stayed the course with her obduracy and Shukracharya had no option but to share the secret of the Sanjivani with Kacha, so that when he came out, killing Shukracharya in the process, he could use the knowledge to bring the old man back to life. Thus, Devayani would have her father as well as her man, and the devas would have access to the Sanjivani as well. From a more commonsensical view, it is interesting to note that it did not seem to strike either father or daughter that Devayani could have been taught the mantra!

In short, for Devayani to have her will, Shukracharya and Kacha had to interact on each other, just as our two keys had to, for the lock to open. The keys have to become one, just as Shukracharya and Kacha had to become one, to provide the solution.

It is a different matter that Kacha then claimed to be Devayani's brother, having issued forth from the womb of her father, and so refused to marry Devayani; and the cad or the braveheart – what you call him will depend on whose side you are – proceeded to Indraloka, with his mission accomplished. But that's another story.

Interdependent Projects

That brings something from the world of project finance to mind. In the world of engineering, a project is defined by its physical characteristics. But in the world of project finance, two projects are regarded as a single composite project if they are interdependent. In such cases, each project by itself may have no sustainability.

For example, we may regard a cement factory and an electric power station as entirely different projects in an engineering sense, calling for two different kinds of expertise and technologies. However, consider a cement plant to be set up in a remote area owing to the proximity of raw material. As there is no electrical power available in that location, the cement plant cannot be operated unless a captive power plant is set up alongside. Financially, neither of the projects makes sense individually. The cash flows of one are dependent on the cash flows of the other, making the two projects interdependent and interacting, which forces us to view the two as a single composite project.

Statistical Interpretations of Interdependence

The problem of interpreting the coefficients of individual variables in the presence of interactions in statistical math is well known. An example may be when, say, the finance manager of an auto company is trying to predict the total revenue from the sales of their subcompact cars, of which they have two models. The sales volumes of the models may be interdependent or correlated because the sales of one model does to some extent eat into the revenues of the other and vice versa. Thus, if you wish to predict the combined sales of the two models, you may need to factor in the interdependence of their revenues, which is to be measured by covariance.

Covariance between two variables is a measure of how much two variables – in this case the sale of the two models – move in tandem. When they move in the same direction, the covariance is positive, and when they move inversely, the covariance is negative. Covariance between two variables is the product of the deviations of corresponding values of the two variables from their respective means.

In mathematical terms,

The covariance between two variables x and y is

$Cov(x,y) = E[\{x - E(x)\}\{y - E(y)\}]$

where E stands for the expected value.

The above may be simplified to:

$Cov(x,y) = E(xy) - E(x)E(y)$.

However, the extent of covariance is not always easy to interpret. One therefore typically resorts to the normalized version of covariance, namely the correlation coefficient, which is nothing but the covariance between the two variables divided by the standard deviation of each variable. But when the variables aren't changing in leaps but vary rather gradually, the problem may well be handled using standard multiple regression method, with the model looking something like this:

$z = ax + by + c$,

where z is the dependent variable, representing total contribution from subcompact cars, and x and y represent the number of the two models of subcompacts sold, while a, b and c are the usual constants. But the regression will not give the desired results unless the covariance between the models is taken into account in interpreting the results.

The problem is equally complex for a locksmith making the keys for the interacting keys. Not only do the keys have to abide by the contours of the lock, they also have to interact on each other, adding to the complexity of making the keys.

Mathematical Modelling of Interdependence

Interdependence has typically been considered as 'the a priori, elusive force at the centre of social interaction'.[1] Mathematical modelling of interdependent variables in social sciences has always remained a challenge. Von Neumann was probably the first mathematician to build a model, albeit a static one, of interdependence in game theory.[2]

Game theory is the theory of social situations which attempts to understand the winning strategies for the parties involved in situations in which their interests are in conflict, as may be expected when those involved are rivals or competitors.

Post Von Neumann, many iterative and dynamic models in social situations have been developed, though these have essentially remained a rapid succession of static models which do not quite capture the interdependent nature of social interactions. Lawless and Sofge note that for statisticians, game theorists and social theorists dealing with social interactions under controlled conditions, the interdependence is a 'nuisance'.[3] This is because assumption of interdependence interferes with the assumption of independence between subjects, which is so essential for replicating experiments under controlled conditions. No wonder the theory of interdependence in social theory has made relatively little headway. For example, many real-life situations do not end with the Nash equilibrium. So what is Nash equilibrium? Now this is like the Mahabharata – a story within a story, or a lock within a lock, if you recall from Chapter 8.

In game theory, Nash equilibrium (named after John Forbes Nash, who proposed it) is a 'solution concept of a game involving two or more players, in which each player is assumed to know the equilibrium strategies of the other players, and no player has anything to gain by changing only his own strategy unilaterally'.[4] Nash equilibrium is supposed to prevail when, if one of the players chooses a strategy such that another player cannot benefit by changing his or her strategy, when all the other players keep their strategies unchanged. The practical and general implication is that when players also act in the interests of the group, then they are better off than if they acted in their individual interests alone.

When Nash Equilibrium Is Not the Standard Equilibrium

Robert Rosenthal developed a game called 'The Centipede', using a chain-store analogy in which a wannabe monopolist operates branches in 100 cities.[5] He faces 100 different competitors in each city. The competitors can choose to *continue* in their business or *opt out* of the city sequentially, that is, one at a time.

If a competitor quietly cooperates yielding the territory to the wannabe monopolist, he receives a payoff of 1, while the monopolist receives a payoff of 5. The monopolist could pay off the competitor with one unit to derive four units of net benefit for himself. If the competitor chooses to defy the monopolist and stand his ground, the monopolist may choose a *cooperative* strategy or an *offensive* one. If he chooses the *cooperative* strategy, in the spirit of live and let live, both the competitor and the monopolist will receive a payoff of 2, and if the monopolist chooses the *offensive* strategy, like resorting to aggressive price cuts to drive the competitor out of the market, both receive 0. Clearly, there is a strange interdependency between the monopolist and the competitor. How would the situation progress?

In an effort to better understand such competitive pricing in the markets, Rosenthal developed a game which, in one of its versions, unfolds as follows:[6]

There are two players – both assumed to be rational and selfish, that is, trying to maximize their personal interests – separated by a partition such that they cannot communicate with each other or even read each other's facial expressions. They have two piles of coins in front of them, say, 4 coins in one and 1 in the other. The first player to make a move has two choices – he may keep the larger pile for himself, leaving the smaller one to the second player or he may pass both piles to the second player. If he opts for the first option, that is, keeping the larger pile, leaving the smaller one for the second player, the game terminates, with the first player receiving 4 coins and the second receiving 1. But if he passes both the piles across the table, 1 coin will be added to each pile, as an external contribution, and it is now the second player's turn. The second player now has the same two choices in turn, and the passing can go on for a fixed number of moves known to the players in advance. Each time both the piles are passed across the table, a coin is added to each pile. Traditionally, the game was played for hundred moves and hence its name, the Centipede.

To illustrate, in the first move, the first player may pass both piles to the second one, so that the piles increase by one coin each, to 5 and 2 respectively. In the second move, the second player may keep the bigger pile of 5 coins, leaving the first player with only 2, or pass both the piles back to the first player. If he goes for the first option, the game terminates. But if he chooses the second option, the piles increase to 6 and 3 coins respectively and then it is back to the first player for the third move. Thus, the game progresses or terminates depending upon the moves of the two contenders.*

A complex behavioural interaction is at play here. If the one player can 'trust' the other player to delay keeping the larger pile for one more round, the first would want to hold on for another round before keeping the larger pile for oneself. A similar thought

* In some versions of the game, the number of coins is doubled in both the piles at each pass; but in such versions, the total number of moves is usually under 10.

process is at play with the other player. The two thought processes are, in some unstated manner, interdependent. I will trust you if you trust me to trust you to trust me ... In short then, every time a player passes both piles across, he faces the risk of his payoff reducing if the opposing player were to terminate the game by keeping the larger pile. This is because the player who passed both the piles will receive less when the opponent terminates the game than he would have, had he terminated the game one move earlier.

In the game-theoretic analogy, passing both the piles across is akin to cooperation, in that it increases the collective pool. Keeping the larger pile and thus terminating the game is akin to defection.

In the game above, the Nash equilibrium predicts that it will terminate in the very first move. Let us see why this should be so, using the backward induction logic.

If the game were to reach the 100th move, the second player will be better off, as he gets to keep 103 coins for himself, leaving 100 to the first player. Since the first player knows this, he will defect in the ninety-ninth move, and thus keep 102 coins for himself, leaving 99 for the second player. The second player knows that the first player will defect in the ninety-ninth move and he will want to defect in the ninety-eighth move, and so on. Proceeding along this logic, it is argued that the first player will defect on the first move, receiving the 4 coins available at the beginning of the game.

In real life, however, when The Centipede is played out, it rarely terminates in the first move. Nor does one normally expect it to. In most cases, the players cooperate for a while and defection happens only after the players are some way into the game. It is equally rare for players to continue cooperating till the hundredth move. Clearly, some complex interdependencies of behaviour are at play. It must be evident to both parties that the payoff for some extent of cooperation in the game is much larger than to defect in the very first move or defecting early in the game.

Incidentally, as the difference between the two piles is increased, the real-life game begins to approach the theoretical equilibrium of first move or early defection. In other words, the mathematical model begins to capture the interdependence of interactions more realistically. For example, imagine the two piles having 100 coins and 1 coin in the two piles instead of 4 and 1, with all the rules remaining the same as before. Clearly, the first player now has a much greater incentive to defect right in the first move, because this player will be reluctant to pass on the two piles (which will increase to 101 and 2 respectively) to the second player, because the threat is very real that the second player will defect immediately, keeping the enlarged pile of 101 for himself or herself, leaving just two coins for the first player. So it is a near certainty that the game in this situation will end in the very first move.

The Centipede is not the only situation where the theoretical model of interdependence fails to explain real-life behaviour. For example, typical game theory experiments predict that every human being should be a free rider, but they are not.

Interdependent Stars

It wouldn't be amiss in the context to refer to two other interacting bodies in the heavens: the binary stars – a term for a 'double star' first coined by Sir William Herschel in 1802. Binary stars are two stars in close proximity that are bound together by gravitational laws to form a single composite system. The bodies orbit each other or around a central mass in such a way that neither has a meaningful existence without the other. Locks with two interacting keys may be rare to find, but in the heavens, it is estimated that about a quarter of all stars are binary stars! And yet, the mathematics of the movement of such binary or double stars may not ever form bedside reading, as this book perhaps could!

Well, if it takes two to tango, it takes two tangling keys to open these locks!

APPENDIX

Exponential functions work something like this: Suppose a company pays interest at the rate of, say, 12 per cent per annum. Another company may choose to pay interest at the half-yearly compounded rate of 6 per cent (=12/2) per six months. This works out to 12.36 per cent per annum [$= (1 + 0.06)^2 - 1$]. Yet another one may choose to pay interest at the quarterly compounded rate of 3 per cent (=12/4) per three months, which is equivalent to 12.55 per cent per annum [$= (1 + 0.03)^4 - 1$], and so on. What if the company chose to pay interest at a weekly compounded rate of 12/52 per cent per week? This is equivalent to an annual rate of 12.73 per cent [$= (1 + 0.12/52)^{52} - 1$]; or the daily compounded rate of 12/365 per cent per day, equivalent to 12.747 per cent per annum [$= (1 + 0.12/365)^{365} - 1$], and so on. With each higher frequency of compounding, the effective annual rate gets higher and higher, but at a smaller and smaller rate.

What if a company chose to compound the interest every fraction of a second, or better still, compound the interest continuously, i.e., every infinitesimally small fraction of a second? This means compounding the interest at the rate of 0.12/n, when *n* approaches an infinitely large number. But if we think that by doing so, one ends up paying a very large effective annual rate of interest, we are mistaken. For example, even at continuous compounding, the effective annual interest rate works out to only about 12.75 per cent. This is nothing but $\left(1+\frac{0.12}{n}\right)^{n}-1$ as n tends to infinity. This can be shown to be $e^{0.12} - 1$, where e is the exponential, whose value tends to 2.71828 …, being a limit, the value keeps extending beyond the five digits of the decimal, but that is about all. One may arrive at more and more accurate value of e as follows:

$$= 1 + 1 + 1/2! + 1/3! + 1/4! \dots \text{ up to infinity,}$$

where 2! means 2 × 1 (pronounced two factorial); 3! means 3 × 2 × 1; 4! means 4 × 3 × 2 × 1, and so on.

NOTES

Chapter 1

1 Hofstadter, D.R., *Metamagical Themas: Questing For the Essence of Mind and Pattern*, Penguin Books, New York, 1985, p 700.

2 The reason why a polynomial of nth degree cannot have more than n distinct roots is because if it did, say r_1, r_2, r_3, ..., and r_{n+1}, then the polynomial of nth degree in x, F(x), should be capable of being factored somewhat as:

$$F(x) = (x - r_1)(x - r_2) \ldots (x - r_{n+1}).$$

However, expanding the polynomial, we would have on our hands a polynomial of n + 1th degree and not of the nth degree. Q.E.D.

3 If $ax^3 + bx^2 + cx + d = 0$, the three roots of the equation (x_1, x_2 and x_3) are given by the following closed-form formulae (The coefficients *a*, *b*, *c* and *d* are generally assumed to be real numbers, but most of the results apply even otherwise).

For the general cubic equation above with real coefficients, the general formulae for the three roots (if there are two non-real roots) are:

$$x_1 = -\frac{b}{3a} - \frac{1}{3a}\sqrt[3]{\frac{1}{2}\left[2b^3 - 9abc + 27a^2d + \sqrt{(2b^3 - 9abc + 27a^2d)^2 - 4(b^2 - 3ac)^3}\right]} - \frac{1}{3a}\sqrt[3]{\frac{1}{2}\left[2b^3 - 9abc + 27a^2d - \sqrt{(2b^3 - 9abc + 27a^2d)^2 - 4(b^2 - 3ac)^3}\right]}$$

$$x_2 = -\frac{b}{3a} + \frac{1 + i\sqrt{3}}{6a}\sqrt[3]{\frac{1}{2}\left[2b^3 - 9abc + 27a^2d + \sqrt{(2b^3 - 9abc + 27a^2d)^2 - 4(b^2 - 3ac)^3}\right]}$$

$$+\frac{1-i\sqrt{3}}{6a}\sqrt[3]{\frac{1}{2}\left[2b^3-9abc+27a^2d-\sqrt{(2b^3-9abc+27a^2d)^2-4(b^2-3ac)^3}\right]}$$

$$x_3=-\frac{b}{3a}$$

$$+\frac{1-i\sqrt{3}}{6a}\sqrt[3]{\frac{1}{2}\left[2b^3-9abc+27a^2d+\sqrt{(2b^3-9abc+27a^2d)^2-4(b^2-3ac)^3}\right]}$$

$$+\frac{1+i\sqrt{3}}{6a}\sqrt[3]{\frac{1}{2}\left[2b^3-9abc+27a^2d-\sqrt{(2b^3-9abc+27a^2d)^2-4(b^2-3ac)^3}\right]}$$

4 http://en.wikipedia.org/wiki/Quartic_function, as on 12 April 2012.

Chapter 3

1 Some sources omit the initial 0, instead beginning the sequence with two 1s.

2 Factorial of n (or n!) = n × (n−1) × (n−2) × (n−3) × … × 3 × 2 × 1. Incidentally, 0! is by definition unity, or 1.

3 ^nC_r or combination of 'n' items taken 'r' at a time is nothing but $\frac{n!}{r!\,(n-r)!}$.

4 Given the quadratic of the form $ax^2 + bx + c = 0$, $x = \frac{-b\pm\sqrt{b^2-4ac}}{2a} = \frac{1\pm\sqrt{5}}{2}$.

Chapter 5

1 Rebecca Sitton's *Spelling Sourcebook* series, Egger Publishing Inc., Scottsdale, 2004.

Chapter 7

1 The do-or-die warriors charged to either slay Arjuna or be slain.

Chapter 8

1 'Straight Dope' by Cecil Adams, www.straightdope.com, 'Reprinted with permission of Creative Loafing, Inc.'

Chapter 9

1 Science Daily,1 September 2008 (http://www.sciencedaily.com/videos/2008/0910-science_of_origami.htm) – as on 7 April 2012.

Chapter 10

1 Jones, E. E. *Interpersonal Perception*, New York, Freeman (1990).
2 Von Neumann, J., and Morgenstern, O., *Theory of Games and Economic Behavior*, Princeton University Press, Princeton (1953).
3 William F. Lawless W. F. and Sofge D. A., 'The Mathematics of Aggregation, Interdependence, Organizations and Systems of Nash Equilibria (NE): A replacement for Game Theory'; presented at the International Conference on Computational Science, Nanyang Technological University, Singapore, 1–3 June 2011.
4 Osborne, Martin J. and Ariel Rubinstein, A *Course in Game Theory*, Cambridge, MA: MIT, 1994.
5 Rosenthal R.W., 'Games of Perfect Information Theory: Predatory Pricing and the Chain Store Paradox', *Journal of Economic Theory* 25, pp 92–100.
6 Also see V. Raghunathan, *Corruption Conundrum and Other Paradoxes and Dilemmas*, Penguin Portfolio, New Delhi (2010), p 56; and *Games Indians Play*, Penguin Portfolio, New Delhi (2006), pp. 32–48.

INDEX